21 DAY
MINDFULNESS & MEDITATION CHALLENGE

Develop Self-Awareness, Reduce Stress
& Manage Negative Emotion

The international best-selling online course,
now available as a book!

Joeel A. Rivera, M.Ed.
& Natalie Rivera

ISBN 978-1-60166-055-8

Check out additional resources for personal growth and at the end of this book! Plus, find out how to become a Certified Mindfulness Life Coach!

Download 10 free MP3 meditations (marked with 🪷) and other resources that accompany this book at https://www.transformationacademy.com/mindfulnessbook

TRANSFORMATION
—— PUBLISHING ——

CONTENTS

SECTION 1: THE POWER OF MINDFULNESS

1: WHY PRACTICE MINDFULNESS

We are passionate about teaching people to develop self-awareness and mindfulness because our ability to remain centered and focused is what has allowed us to thrive through even the most challenging parts of our lives. In fact, when I (Joeel) was sick and bed ridden for a year, I used many of the mindfulness skills in this book to help me find peace and joy in the darkest places. During my many emergency room visits, doctors wondered how I would be laughing and joking around with Natalie while my body was basically shutting down. The reason we could maintain that attitude was because mindfulness helped us let go of negative mental chatter and focus on the present moment.

We also know what it is like in those moments when we were not able to remain mindful and got swept away in worry and despair. Mindfulness is a skill that can be developed, and doing so changed our lives. That is why we are so excited to share these powerful tools with you.

Nearly all people who are extremely successful, including most professional athletes, use mindfulness and meditation because study after study have revealed the amazing benefits! Mindfulness and meditation have been shown to change the areas of the brain associated with memory, learning and regulation of emotion. This leads to increased mental clarity and concentration, reduced stress, and increased experiences of peace and happiness. Plus, it's been shown to have powerful health benefits, including improving sleep, raising energy, increasing immune function, lowering blood pressure and reducing headaches.

Studies have also shown that people spend almost 50% of their daily life on autopilot, meaning that you probably missing out on your life because you're lost in thought, worry, or stress. And if you're like most people, you probably put countless energy and money into things that you believe will help you be happier, healthier, and live longer. But what if we told you that there is one simple thing that you can do every day that will not only help you extend your life but will help you actually experience more OF your life? There is! MINDFULNESS.

If you are tired of being stressed out, frustrated, unable to stop negative thinking, and you're ready to finally live fully aware, awake, and alive, then we invite you to take the 21 Day Mindfulness, Meditation and Self-Awareness Challenge!

In just 20 minutes a day, for 3 weeks, you will learn mindfulness and meditation techniques that will help you master your monkey mind, reduce stress, manage negative emotions, and enjoy your life more.

Here is what you will be doing in the 21 Day Challenge:

- In Week 1 you'll practice enjoying the present moment and learning how to be mindful in everyday life.
- In Week 2 you'll learn to be the observer of your thoughts and emotions so you can master your monkey mind and manage negative emotions.
- In Week 3 you'll take what you've learned and use it to develop self-compassion, take back control of what and who you allow to influence you, and practice being more present with others.

And, if you prefer not to learn mindfulness in a structured program like this, feel free to peruse through the book and use the exercises and meditations however you wish, at your own pace.

2: CULTIVATING MINDFULNESS AND SELF-AWARENESS

"The outer situation of your life and whatever happens there is the surface of the lake. Sometimes calm, sometimes windy and rough, according to the cycles and seasons. Deep down, however, the lake is always undisturbed. You are the whole lake, not just the surface." – Eckhart Tolle

For most people, the chaos and noise happening around them and within their own minds feels like all there is. They live in a constant state of reactivity, being pushed and pulled by the thoughts and emotions they experience. They're controlled by a voice in their head that worries about everything that can go wrong, criticizes them for everything they do wrong, and feels guilty or angry about everything that went wrong. This voice interprets every situation instantaneously and we don't question it, just like we don't question our breathing. It all happens unconsciously, meaning we are unaware of it. And then we feel and act based on the voice's interpretation.

The truth is that everyone has a voice in their head, including you. Some people's voices are nicer than others, but everyone's voice tends to have the same disfunctions. But the good news—perhaps the best news anyone can ever hear is that this voice is not who you are.

For some of the people reading this book, you already know this well. For others, it may be the first time you have heard it, or the first time you truly understand it. If you've ever argued with yourself over something or you've ever noticed yourself thinking about something ridiculous or you've ever talked to yourself in your own mind, then you've experienced that there are two of you. There is the one that does the thinking, feeling, and reacting and there is the one that is aware of the thoughts, emotions, and reactions. You are that awareness. You are the presence that witnesses the voice, but you are not the voice.

Knowing this allows you to observe what your inner voice is doing and thinking. This is called self-observation or self-awareness. As you become more and more aware of what has always been going on unconsciously, beneath the surface of your awareness, you become conscious. You wake up from the dream. And the process for developing this awareness is called mindfulness.

Until you develop self-awareness and mindfulness, you will likely live much of your life on auto pilot, feeling like you have little control over your thoughts, emotions, or life. The truth is that unless you know what you're thinking, feeling, or doing, you have no way of changing it.

Simply developing this awareness is the key that unlocks all of your power. Power to direct your own inner voice, choose better-feeling emotions, and making better decisions.

Start by listening to the voice in your head as often as you can. Pay particular attention to any thoughts that repeat. Be the observer of what is happening inside of you—both the surface of the lake and the depths. See if you can find and feel the deep calm at the bottom of the lake even when the surface is rough.

As you practice mindfulness and observing your thoughts and reactions, you'll be able to recognize even more clearly that the presence doing the observing is the true you. When you notice yourself feeling angry, you'll observe that the angry part and the part observing it are not the same thing. This is important to know because your true self never becomes disrupted and entangled in these surface level dramas. There is a part of you that is at peace, content, safe, and joyful no matter what is going on around you and in your mind. Your higher self is untouchable, un-disruptable. Knowing it is always there means you can seek to find it in any moment.

And, just like when the sun dips below the horizon you know that it still exists, even though you cannot see it, this calm, peaceful presence that is you is always there, even if you cannot see it.

As you begin to pay attention with a sense of curiosity to discover what your inner voice is up to, you'll begin to notice interesting things it does. You'll notice when you are behaving in a way that is in alignment with your goals and our values, and when you are not. You'll notice when you are smiling even though you are actually sad, or when you say you are fine even though you are not. You may notice you are pretending to be mad when you really aren't, just to manipulate someone else's behavior. Or, you may notice that you are thinking negative thoughts about yourself, making you feel insecure. You may even notice when we are soothing yourself or feeling relaxed or happy.

The last thing you need to know about cultivating mindfulness before we move on is that the doorway to all awareness is the present moment. Most people's minds have a strong habit of spending a lot of time thinking about the past or imagining, and usually worrying about, the future. But, the power to observe and redirect your thoughts, emotions, and behaviors is only accessible when you are focused on the present moment. When you're paying attention to what is going on in this moment, you can notice the mind remembering an experience from the past or worrying about the future. But, if yourself to go with your mind TO these past or future places, you lose your sense of awareness. For this reason, one excellent way to develop mindfulness and self-awareness is to pay attention as often as you can to what is happening RIGHT NOW. Pay attention to each step you take, to the noises going on around you, to your breathing. Once you pull your awareness back into the present moment, it gives you an opportunity to notice what you're thinking.

It is also important for you to know that the next time you notice yourself experiencing a negative thought or emotion, it doesn't mean you've failed—it means you've succeeded! Until you are able to become aware of these negative experiences you have little power over them. Every time you notice a negative thought, celebrate! Give yourself a high five! Because now you know that this negative thought is NOT who you are. You are the one in charge! Throughout the rest of this book, you will be learning how to develop this awareness and use proven tools to change the content of your inner world.

3: USE MINDFULNESS TO CHANGE EMOTIONS IN 90 SECONDS

90 seconds is all it takes to shift out of a negative emotion. The catch is that you have to not FEED it for 90 seconds for it to fade away. Another way to look at it is if you shift your attention to a different focus, thought or emotion for 90 seconds, you'll switch out of the original emotion and into the next one.

You might be thinking that 90 seconds sounds really short, considering how long you can get stuck in a bad mood. But the truth is that it can be that easy, that is, once you learn how to direct your focus.

You see, emotions are simply what we feel due to a biochemical reaction in our bodies. These rushes of emotion are transitory, meaning temporary. If not perpetuated, they will pass in about 90 seconds. So, what keeps emotions, especially negative ones like anger, cycling for minutes, hours or even days?

Here is the key—the cause of the biochemical reaction that we call emotion is our thoughts. They can be conscious thoughts (the ones we know we're thinking) or unconscious thoughts (such as beliefs or programming that we don't realize are active within us). These thoughts send a signal to our brain as to what we should feel and the flood of chemicals ensues.

If you haven't already figured out where we're going with this, here it is: by continuing to think about whatever it is that triggered the emotion you continue to feed the emotion. You keep it active by continuing to dwell on it, like stewing in your own brain chemical soup! This is great news because this means that by stopping the thoughts that feed the emotion, the emotion will subside.

Let's look at an example of how this works. Have you ever had a conversation with someone, especially one that was heated, and then hours after you stopped interacting with them you find yourself continuing the conversation in your head? The problem with this is that as long as you keep thinking about the conversation, the longer your brain thinks the argument is happening because your brain doesn't know the difference between what is happening and what you are imagining. The result is that you continue feeling angry.

The solution is to become more mindful. Throughout this book, we will be reviewing a number of techniques to become aware of the negative emotions and consciously release and shift them. Not only can you use what you learn to stop yourself from replaying unwanted conversations in your head, you can use it to keep better control of your thoughts and emotions during the real-time conversation, too.

4: THE 3 CORE SKILLS OF MINDFULNESS

In order to live your life mindfully and develop self-awareness, there are three core skills that you need to develop: 1) focused attention or concentration, 2) open monitoring or present moment awareness, and 3) acceptance or non-judgment. Let's look at what each of these mean:

Focused Attention (Concentration)

Focused attention is like paying attention "on purpose". Throughout the book you will hear us use the word "awareness" and know that when we say awareness we are usually talking about deliberate, focused attention. Think about it like concentrating on something, which means consciously choosing what we're paying attention to. For example, you may know that you are eating but your mind can be thinking about a hundred other things, watching TV, talking, or playing with your phone. A very small part of your awareness is absorbed in eating. This is very different from eating mindfully, or with focused attention. When you eat mindfully you are fully aware of your eating—you deliberately notice the sensations, flavors, textures. When your mind wanders, you bring your attention back to eating.

Developing focused attention does not have to be complicated. Being fully aware of a single breath can take you there, and we take 8 to 10 million breaths a year, so we have a lot of opportunities.

Open Monitoring (Present Moment Awareness)

Unlike focused attention when you direct your awareness at just one thing, open monitoring is observing whatever is happening at the moment. Focused attention is like having tunnel vision, while open monitoring is like looking through a wide angle lens.

When we practice mindfulness, our thoughts are focused on what we're sensing in the present moment rather than rehearsing the past or imagining the future. It's about paying attention to NOW, which is the one moment we actually can. This is perhaps the most important reason to practice mindfulness because when you stay stuck in a state of mindlessness, lost in thought about the past or future, you are letting your life pass you by. Mindfulness means living in the moment and truly experiencing life. Like we said, mindfulness is concerned with focusing on what's going on right now. That doesn't mean we can no longer think about the past or future, but when we do so we do so mindfully, meaning that we're aware in the moment that we're thinking about the past or future. There is a higher level of awareness that comes in.

Acceptance (Non-Judgment)

Mindfulness involves acceptance, meaning that we observe our thoughts and feelings without judging them. We stop believing that there's a "right" or "wrong" way to think or feel in a given moment. It means we don't beat ourselves up when we catch ourselves thinking about things we didn't want to think about. It also involves acceptance of the conditions of life, as well as other people. Mindfulness means learning how to accept what IS, see the truth clearly, and stop living in resistance. By seeing things as they are, without judging them, you will be able to make peace with them and choose healthy ways of responding.

And, when you put all three of these skills together and you are able to live mindfully, it is like being awakened from a dream. Suddenly you can see things more clearly. You appreciate the everyday miracles. You can observe your thoughts and reactions and deliberately choose how to respond to life situations. You have greater compassion for others and you're no longer so tense because you've made peace with life. And, most importantly, you become fully aware of yourself. And with your heightened level of self-awareness you will feel more confident, knowing that you have the power to direct your own life. You will have more compassion for yourself, and you will no longer beat yourself up for your negative thoughts or feelings. You will see your mind like a puppy who doesn't always listen and sometimes makes messes, but you will have the same loving kindness toward yourself as you teach your mind how to master itself.

Mindfulness Skill	Related Mindfulness and Meditation Exercises
FOCUSED ATTENTION (CONCENTRATION)	Day 1: 2-Minute Bell Exercise, 3-Minute Breathing Space, Square Breathing
	Day 2: Candle Meditation
	Day 3: Body Awareness, Progressive Relaxation
	Day 4: Mindful Eating, Mindful Curiosity
	Day 5: Music Meditation
OPEN MONITORING (PRESENT MOMENT AWARENESS)	Day 1: The Mini-Mindfulness Exercise, Simple Mindfulness Meditation
	Day 2: The 5 Senses Exercise, Mindful Seeing Exercise
	Day 5: Mindful Listening
	Day 6: Mindful Walking
	Day 7: Mindful Driving
	Day 8: Observing Your Train of Thought
	Day 9: Sorting Thoughts into Boxes, Urge Management
	Day 10: Self-Talk Activity
	Day 15: Self-Inquiry Meditation
	Day 18: Holding Space, Mindful Arrivals
ACCEPTANCE (NON-JUDGMENT)	Day 3: Progressive Relaxation
	Day 5: Mindful Listening
	Day 8: Observing Your Train of Thought
	Day 9: Sorting Thoughts into Boxes, Urge Management

	Day 11: RAIN Technique for Accepting Emotions
	Day 12: Mindfulness for Anger, Willing Hands Meditation
	Day 13: The Half Smile, Gratitude Meditation
	Day 14: Release/Surrender Meditation
	Day 16: Self-Compassion Exercise, Mindfulness Mountain Meditation
	Day 18: Holding Space
	Day 19: Loving Kindness Meditation

5: MINDFULNESS AND MEDITATION (AND 7 COMMON MYTHS)

Mindfulness and meditation are both practices for calming the mind, focusing attention, and creating peace of mind. The words are often used interchangeably, however they are different. There are also common misunderstandings about meditation, and some people have resistance to it. Let's take a closer look at what mindfulness and meditation really are.

Mindfulness is a state of heightened awareness and deliberate focus on the present moment. You can be mindful of your breath, what you're doing, what your senses observe, or your own internal thoughts and emotions. Mindfulness practices usually include focusing your mind intentionally, focusing on your breathing, and quieting your mind.

Ultimately, meditation is the same thing, only it is a bit more formal. Rather than simply bringing your awareness to whatever is going on, meditation follows a specific process. Normally you are seated or lying down and in a place where you can spend a longer period of time (at least 5 minutes) without being disrupted. Meditation is taking mindfulness to a deeper level. It is usually directed more internally, rather than observing the outside world. And it's more deliberate.

Think of it like this: mindfulness is broader, focuses internally and externally, and can be practiced any time, anywhere, while meditation is more specifically focused internally and is practiced more deliberately and formally. By formal, we mean both that they are more structured, such as following a step-by-step guided meditation, and more regular, such as practicing meditation at the same time every day.

Throughout this book you will find exercises labeled MEDITATION. They will help you bring your awareness into your breath, your body, your imagination and your mind. These are interactive exercises that you can read to yourself or record in your own voice. Many of these meditations are available as downloads at: https://www.transformationacademy.com/mindfulnessbook.

Because some people are skeptical or resistant to meditation, before we continue let's take a look at the **Top 7 Common Myths about Meditation:**

1. **I don't know how to do it.** Many people fear doing meditation wrong, but the truth is that it is as simple as paying attention to your own breathing. There is no ultimate goal of meditation or any right way to do it, so relax and know you can't mess this up!

2. **To meditate I have to stop thinking and have a blank mind.** It is impossible to completely stop thinking. Even the most advanced meditators can only reduce their thinking. It is true that part of the purpose of meditating is to quiet and calm the mind so that you can have more control over it, but thinking while you're meditating isn't a problem. Having your mind wander and think about what you're going to eat for lunch is totally normal. When you notice it, simply redirect it back at the meditation practice. Over time your mind will naturally stay focused better, which is the point! But don't go into it wanting your thoughts to stop. If they stopped you would miss out on all the great benefits of meditation, including being able to more clearly OBSERVE those thoughts.

3. **Meditation means sitting in awkward positions that require you to be flexible.** Yes, some people do that, but it is a stereotyped image not reality. Most people meditate sitting in a chair, lying down, standing or even walking. While it's ideal to have good posture, it's really about being still in a comfortable position.

4. **Meditation is religious, spiritual or "woo-woo".** Although often associated with Buddhism, Hinduism, or hippy, new-agey spiritualism, nearly all cultures and religions have practices that are considered meditation, although they often call it by a different name. Meditation has become mainstream and secular (meaning it's not religious or spiritual) due to the numerous studies proving its

effectiveness at reducing stress and anxiety and boosting productivity and happiness. Nearly all successful (financially and happily) leaders report that meditation is part of their life and professional athletes use it as part of their conditioning routines. None of the meditations in this book discuss any symbolism, concepts or beliefs of any kind that are spiritual or religious in nature.

5. **I don't want people to hear me chanting or saying "OM".** Again, yes, some people do include vocalization in their meditations, but you do not have to. None of the meditations in this book will require you to make any noise of any kind.

6. **People who meditate are always peaceful.** Although statistically someone who meditates is more likely to feel content, peaceful, happy, and focused, by no means does that mean they don't have stress, anger, or occasionally go squirrel.

7. **You have to be relaxed or Zen to meditate. Type-A's or people with anxiety can't meditate.** This is just not true. In fact, people who are high strung, high energy, anxious, or have attention deficit can benefit from meditation even more than others. Again, you can't do meditation wrong. Some people, especially people who practice meditation a lot over a long period of time, can get into a deeper state of relaxation than others. However, no matter who you are, taking the time to practice breathing techniques and focus your mind has positive effects and will result in a calmer mind and wellbeing.

6: 3 TYPES OF MEDITATION: FORMAL, INFORMAL AND RETREAT

There are 3 types of meditation: informal, formal and intensive retreat. Choosing the right type of practice in important because you may be seeking results that not all types of meditation will achieve.

Informal meditation is being mindful of whatever you are doing at the moment, such as going for a walk and noticing every step you take. It is also unstructured, meaning there is no routine.

- The benefit of this type of meditation is that you can do it any time, anywhere, and be called upon in the moment that you need a reset.
- If your goal is to be more tuned-in, alert, and peaceful in your

daily experience, this form of meditation will get you these results.

Formal meditation is more routine and deliberate, such as meditating for 10 minutes every day at 10am and using pre-determined techniques.

- The benefit of this type of meditation is that it becomes a habit or ritual, helping the pattern of thinking and focus required for meditation become unconscious and automatic.
- If your goal is to rewire your though and emotion patterns, shift your emotional setpoint, reduce stress, and improve your overall wellbeing, this type of meditation will get you these results.

Intensive retreat meditation is when you conduct a large amount of meditation in a short period of time, such as several hours or days.

- The benefit of this type of meditation is that it allows you to explore further and experience deeper levels of the meditative state. If conducting intensive meditation in a retreat setting, there is the added benefit of being free of distractions and in an environment that allows you to focus intensely on the practice.
- If your goal is to explore the depths of your unconscious mind and the realm of the spiritual and/or heighten your senses and strengthen your ability to sustain the meditative state, this type of meditation will get you these results.

Research has been conducted in fields such as professional sports, some areas of medicine, and the corporate world (all of which use mindfulness and meditation extensively) showing the dramatic changes in health and wellbeing experienced by people who develop a meditation practice. However, according to research, not all meditation is created equal. Research clearly shows that if you are looking for long-term benefits of mindfulness and meditation, establishing a formal practice is the key. Mindfulness is like a muscle—you need to exercise it regularly to strengthen your mind. As you practice meditation, you will reprogram your automatic thoughts and physically rewire the circuits in your brain. Your central nervous system will learn how to switch off the sympathetic nervous system ("fight or flight" stress response) faster and sustain the parasympathetic nervous system ("rest and digest") response.

As with any new activity, it takes time to develop the skill, which is another reason the formal practice is the most important piece. You will find that the more you practice, the more you will want to do it!

Ideally, you will have the opportunity to utilize all 3 types of meditation. In this book, we will focus on informal mindfulness and formal meditation practices. Feel free to explore the techniques and activities and determine which ones get you the results you are looking for. If you are new, we recommend starting out with simple mindfulness exercises, which is why the activities in this 21 Day Mindfulness and Meditation Challenge starts off with simple exercises and evolves into more advanced meditations as the weeks go on. And, of course, we recommend establishing a routine, so you can take advantage of the proven benefits of a formal meditation practice.

7: HOW TO TAKE THE 21 DAY MINDFULNESS CHALLENGE

This program is designed to evolve from simple awareness exercises and meditation practices up through to deeper insights and processes. It is also intended to be completed in 21 days. However, you are welcome to use the mindfulness and meditation activities throughout the book in whatever order you prefer and in any timeframe! The goal of this book is to provide you with the tools and the inspiration to commit to shift the way you experience your life!

Why 21 days?

Studies have shown that doing a new activity for at LEAST 21 days helps form a habit by creating new neural pathways in the brain. The habit is even more likely to stick if you add it onto an existing habit, which we will explain in a moment.

The reason this program is called a CHALLENGE is that it takes deliberate EFFORT to do it! The truth is, it can be hard to commit to a new habit, even when we KNOW how much joy and peace of mind it will bring to our lives. Take this program seriously and take a minute now to write down or schedule in your daily sessions. Be highly recommend taking the CHALLENGE and committing to mindfulness activities for 21 days, but if you know you cannot complete it in 21 days, that's okay—just schedule it in whatever way works for you.

This book is organized into 3 sections, each containing 7 days of insights and activities. The first week focuses on awareness of the present moment and practicing a variety of mindfulness and meditation activities. The second week focuses on awareness of thoughts and emotions, as you turn your awareness inward and learn how to be the observer of your thoughts and how to both calm and cultivate your emotions. The third week focuses on awareness of yourself and awareness with others, meaning you'll dig even deeper into self-awareness and look more closely at how you are, or are not, present with others. You'll wrap up the challenge by creating a plan for carrying forward your newfound mindfulness into your daily life.

Each day includes a discussion and an activity for the day. Some days you will find multiple activities or meditations. On average it will take 20 minutes per day, however several days will take longer and some are short instructions followed by an action you will take out in your daily life.

We recommend planning a consistent time every day to work on your mindfulness challenge. Before you proceed, decide when you will begin the challenge and when you will commit to completing the exercises every day. The BEST way to integrate a new activity to your life is to add it in just before or just after another routine or habit that you already have. This could mean doing it immediately when you wake up or just before you go to bed. Or maybe you could do it during your lunch break or after you watch your favorite TV or Netflix show. Whenever you decide to practice your mindfulness every day, make sure you make it official. Take out your day planner if you use one and write it into every day that you will be taking the challenge. Set a reminder alarm in your phone to go off every day at the time you decide you will do this. If you're going to invite anyone to join you for the challenge, reach out to them now and set a start date and daily check-in time.

8: 21 DAY MINDFULNESS CHALLENGE SCHEDULE

On average, the mindfulness challenge exercises each day will take 20 minutes. For each day, the total estimated time is noted, including reading time and other actions that will need to be taken while going about your daily life.

WEEK 1: Mindful Awareness of the Present Moment

Day 1: Present Moment Awareness
(READING: 20 minutes | OTHER: 0 minutes)

- MEDITATION: 2-Minute Bell Exercise
- The Mini-Mindfulness Exercise
- 3-Minute Breathing Space
- Simple Mindfulness Meditation
- Square Breathing

Day 2: Shifting from the Thinking Mind to the Sensing Mind
(READING: 25 minutes | OTHER: 10 minutes)

- The 5 Senses Exercise
- Mindful Seeing Exercise
- MEDITATION: Candle Meditation

Day 3: Body Awareness
(READING: 20 minutes | OTHER: 0 minutes)

- MEDITATION: Body Awareness Meditation
- MEDITATION: Progressive Relaxation Meditation

Day 4: Mindful Eating (READING: 6 minutes | OTHER: 5 minutes)

- Mindful Curiosity (Using the Senses)

Day 5: Mindful Listening (READING: 8 minutes | OTHER: 0 minutes)

- Music Meditation

Day 6: Mindful Walking (READING: 4 minutes | OTHER: 10 minutes)

Day 7: Mindful Driving (READING: 4 minutes | OTHER: 10 minutes)

WEEK 2: Awareness of Thoughts and Emotions

Day 8: The Psychology of the Monkey Mind

(READING: 22 minutes | OTHER: 10 minutes)

- Mindfulness of Thoughts (and How They Create Emotions)
- Observing Your Train of Thought

Day 9: Sorting Thoughts into Boxes Exercise

(READING: 7 minutes | OTHER: 0 minutes)

- Urge Management (Urge Surfing)

Day 10: Awareness of Self-Talk

(READING: 15 minutes | OTHER: 10 minutes)

- Awareness of Self-Talk, Part 2

Day 11: Developing Emotional Awareness

(READING: 8 minutes | OTHER: 0 minutes)

- RAIN Technique for Accepting Emotions

Day 12: Mindfulness for Anger and Other Negative Emotions

(READING: 11 minutes | OTHER: 10 minutes)

- Willing Hands

Day 13: Intentionally Creating Desired Emotions

(READING: 27 minutes | OTHER: 0 minutes)

- The Half Smile Technique
- The Power of Gratitude
- MEDITATION: Gratitude Meditation

Day 14: Surrender, Acceptance, and Letting Go

(READING: 20 minutes | OTHER: 0 minutes)

- MEDITATION: Release/Surrender Meditation

WEEK 3: Awareness of Self and With Others

Day 15: Everything We Experience is Internal

(READING: 16 minutes | OTHER: 0 minutes)

- MEDITATION: Self-Inquiry Meditation

Day 16: Self-Compassion Exercise

(READING: 8 minutes | OTHER: 0 minutes)

- MEDITATION: Mindfulness Mountain Meditation

Day 17: The Importance of Choosing Inputs

(READING: 7 minutes | OTHER: 10 minutes)

- Day 18: Being Present with Others and Holding Space
- Mindful Arrivals

Day 19: Random Acts of Kindness

(READING: 15 minutes | OTHER: 0 minutes)

- MEDITATION: Loving-Kindness Meditation

Day 20: Developing a Mindfulness Routine

(READING: 24 minutes | OTHER: 10 minutes)

- Mindful Morning Routine
- Mindful Bedtime Routine

Day 21: Creating a Formal Meditation Practice

(READING: 10 minutes | OTHER: 10 minutes)

9: 21 DAY MINDFULNESS JOURNAL

WEEK 1: MINDFUL AWARENESS OF THE PRESENT MOMENT

Day 1: Present Moment Awareness

My biggest takeaways:

My favorite mindfulness or meditation activity:

Other thoughts:

Day 2: Shifting from the Thinking Mind to the Sensing Mind

My biggest takeaways:

My favorite mindfulness or meditation activity:

Other thoughts:

Day 3: Body Awareness

My biggest takeaways:

Other thoughts or observations about the body awareness exercises:

Day 4: Mindful Eating

My biggest takeaways:

Other thoughts or observations:

Day 5: Mindful Listening

My biggest takeaways:

My favorite song, music genre, or other sounds to listen to:

Other thoughts:

Day 6: Mindful Walking

My biggest takeaways:

My favorite part of mindful walking:

Other thoughts:

Day 7: Mindful Driving

My biggest takeaways:

My favorite part of mindful driving:

Other thoughts:

WEEK 2: AWARENESS OF THOUGHTS AND EMOTIONS

Day 8: The Psychology of the Monkey Mind

Practicing Observing Trains of Thought Step-By-Step:

- A train of thought comes in
- Identify it ("I notice I'm having the thought that…")
- Now watch it leave, without engaging it
- Repeat for every thought that enters your mind (for as long as you can stand)

My biggest takeaways:

My observations and experience of watching a train of thoughts:

The most challenging part of this exercise:

Other thoughts:

Day 9: Sorting Thoughts into Boxes Exercise and Urge Surfing

My biggest takeaways:

My experience with the thought sorting exercise:

My experience with the urge surfing exercise:

Other thoughts:

Day 10: Awareness of Self-Talk (See Full Activity)

My biggest takeaways:

Other thoughts:

Day 11: Developing Emotional Awareness (See Full Activity)

My biggest takeaways:

What emotions I struggle the most to accept:

My experience with the RAIN exercise:

Other thoughts:

Day 12: Mindfulness for Anger and Other Negative Emotions

My biggest takeaways:

My experience with the willing hands exercise:

Other thoughts:

Day 13: Intentionally Creating Desired Emotions (See Full Cultivation Activity)

My biggest takeaways:

My thoughts on creating emotions and the cultivation circle activity:

My thoughts on the half-smile:

My thoughts on gratitude:

Day 14: Surrender, Acceptance, and Letting Go

My biggest takeaways:

Thoughts, emotions, situations, memories, grudges I can surrender:

My experience with the surrender meditation:

Other thoughts:

WEEK 3: AWARENESS OF SELF AND WITH OTHERS

Day 15: Everything We Experience is Internal/Self-Inquiry Meditation

My biggest takeaways:

My experience with the self-inquiry meditation:

Other thoughts:

Day 16: Self-Compassion Exercise

My biggest takeaways:

My thoughts on self-compassion:

My experience with the mountain meditation:

Other thoughts:

Day 17: The Importance of Choosing Inputs (See Full Activity)

My biggest takeaways:

Other thoughts:

Day 18: Being Present with Others/Holding Space (See Full Activity)

My biggest takeaways:

My experience being mindful during arrivals:

Other thoughts:

Day 19: Random Acts of Kindness

My biggest takeaways:

Random acts of kindness I did today (or will do):

My experience with the loving kindness meditation:

Other thoughts:

Day 20: Developing a Mindfulness Routine (See Full Activity)

My Mindful Morning Routine:

My Mindful Bedtime Routine:

Other thoughts:

Day 21: Creating a Formal Meditation Practice (See Full Activity)

My desires for my formal meditation practice:

Other thoughts:

WEEK 1: MINDFUL AWARENESS OF THE PRESENT MOMENT

DAY 1: PRESENT MOMENT AWARENESS

THE MINI-MINDFULNESS EXERCISE

Another great activity to become more mindful when you are short on time is the mindfulness exercise. This activity has three simple steps that you can do anywhere.

- **Step 1:** Bring awareness to your thoughts, what you are doing and sensing in your environment. Try to be in a comfortable position and notice your thoughts without judging them, and let them come to awareness and let them pass by.
- **Step 2:** Now bring your awareness to your breath. Take the time to focus on six breaths or for a minute. Become aware of the air coming in and out of your lungs and how your body is moved by it. For example, how does your chest rise and fall?
- **Step 3:** Next expand awareness to the rest of your body to your current environment. Notice any sensation in your body and then move to your 5 senses of what is in your environment. What are the colors, shapes, patterns, sounds, tastes, feeling that your senses are picking up?

When you are done take a deep breath and try to keep that awareness of your environment as long as you can. You can do this throughout the day to get re-centered quickly.

3-MINUTE BREATHING SPACE

There are times that you just need a quick way to get re-centered or you just want a mindful practice that you can practice quickly. Therefore, unlike other mindful practices this one can be done easily and quickly especially for those people that have a busy life and an active mind. This activity has three process and each of them takes about a minute. See the process below.

1. The first step in the process is taking a minute and asking yourself "how am I doing right now?". During this time focus on the feelings, sensations, and thoughts that may arise while giving them words and phrases associated with them.

2. In the second step or second minute you will spend it on focusing on you on your breath. Do not try to change it, just develop awareness of it.

3. In the last minute you will expand your focus from just your breath to focusing on the rest of your body and how your breath affects the rest of your body.

Keep in mind that it may be normal for your mind to wander. Therefore, do not judge it or try to block them. Just observe the thoughts let it come in and let it disappear. Also keep in mind that the more you do any sort of these activities that create mindfulness the easier it will become. In fact, you are training your mind and like any other training it may take some time.

2-MINUTE BELL EXERCISE

Let's jump right in with our first mindfulness exercise! In this exercise, you will use the sound of a repeating bell to anchor your attention in the present moment. This is a great, quick way to re-focus and calm your mind. Consider using this bell-exercise every day to start your mindfulness process and complete the activities in this 21 Day Challenge. The repetition will turn the sound of this bell into a powerful anchor that will immediately ground you and pull your awareness into the present moment.

Close your eyes now. As you listen, notice the intensity of the bell when it rings and then stay with the sounds as it fades away.

SIMPLE MINDFULNESS MEDITATION

The term "meditation" often conjures up images of sitting cross-legged on the floor, surrounded by crystals, in a dimly lit room that smells like incense. For some people, this sounds appealing and for others, they assume meditation is a weird, woo-woo, airy fairy experience. But, the truth is that meditation is simply a process of observing and quieting your mind. If you don't like the word meditation, call it focusing.

This exercise helps people disengage from obsessive thinking, which means thoughts that have a lot of momentum, by paying attention to the present moment. There has been a significant amount of research conducted on this form of meditation and the positive effects it has on a number of psychological problems.

Simple mindfulness meditation practice:

- Find a quiet place free of distractions. Your mind will offer enough distractions of its own, so pick a place where no one will interrupt you.
- Sit comfortably in any position you desire. Upright is ideal, however you can lay down if you want to. Just make sure your position is comfortable and will not distract you.
- Start by bringing your attention to your breathing. Notice the sensation of your breath entering and exiting your nose or mouth. Notice how it feels as the air brushes through. Is it cool? Does it tingle?
- Notice the rise and fall of your chest or abdomen as the air fills and then empties your lungs. Do not force or control your breathing, simply allow it to be natural and continue to observe it.
- Watch your breathing for about 5 minutes. During this time, you will find that your mind will wander off and think about all sorts of things: physical sensations, things you need to do, what happened yesterday. This is totally normal. When you notice your mind has wondered off, simply start noticing your breathing again. You may need to bring it back again and again, and this is wonderful because it means you are becoming mindful!
- The more you practice this, the less your mind will wander. Then, you'll notice you are better able to keep your focus at other times throughout the day as well!

- When you are finished with your 5 minutes, you may notice an increased sense of calm.

- As you get used to this activity, you can increase the time sitting to 10, 15, or 20 minutes. What is most important is consistency, so regardless of how long you sit in this mindful state, do it every day.

- The most important point of developing a daily meditation practice is consistency, so 3 minutes every day is better than an hour once a week.

Next, we'll be looking at additional mindfulness, breathing, and meditation techniques. For a more advanced guided meditation practice, do the Guided Progressive Relaxation exercise.

SQUARE BREATHING

As you discovered in the mindfulness meditation, paying attention to your breathing can help increase focus and decrease stress. This square breathing technique is another method to focus the mind, this time using controlled, deliberate breathing.

Square breathing is very simple. A square has four equal sides. Square breathing has four equal sections. Inhale for 4 seconds, hold it for 4 seconds, exhale for 4 seconds, and then hold for 4 seconds again, and then repeat. If you find it hard to hold your breath for 4 seconds in this cycle, count to 3 when going around your square instead.

It can also be helpful to imagine moving along the edges of a square object, so visualize yourself breathing around the 4 corners of a square, a box, a window, a photo frame, or anything else that's square.

Looking for a simple way to melt away tension during a stressful day? Need a break so you can refocus your attention? Square breathing is a simple and effective way to calm yourself down in the moment when you meet it, plus you can enjoy a few minutes of peace.

Continue this activity for a minimum of 5 minutes and as you get used to it, expand the amount of time you continue this breathing pattern to 10 or 15 minutes.

DAY 2: SHIFTING FROM THE THINKING MIND TO THE SENSING MIND

One of the key aspects of being mindful is being able to step away from the thinking mind and embracing the sensing mind. Many times, people get caught up in thoughts and feelings which may create stress, anxiety, depression, or distraction. Many times, we think that if we take action or consume our self with thinking about something that in some magic way things will be fixed. However, sometimes there is nothing that we can do about it and spending time obsessing over those things can be counter-productive and cause unnecessary stress. The human mind tends to keep itself busy and thinking about the past or the future, unless we train it to be here now—to be mindful. The thinking mind is the one that gets wrapped up in thoughts while the sensing mind is the one we can activate by choosing to focus on our senses which bring us into awareness of what is going on around us in the present moment.

Shifting into the sensing mind is like shifting out of "doing" mode and into "being" mode.

When we are using our sensing mind we are not trying to do something we are just being and we are free to enjoy our life experiences from moment to moment. Being in this state gives us space and an ability to decrease stress. For example, you have probably been in a situation where you should be having fun but you're not because instead of enjoying the moment you are thinking about something that happened in the past or worrying about the future. In contrast, you've probably experienced times when you were fully engaged in your environment and all your problems seem to disappear from your awareness.

The reality is that you have finite energy and focus, and you can only be in one world or another—the here and now or lost in thought. In any moment you can choose either to focus on the stress of the day and think about what problems you need to deal with OR turn your attention to what your senses are experiencing, your breathing, or what's going on around you. Like most people, your mind probably has a strong habit of thinking about things that aren't happening now, but you can train it by practicing.

The simple act of becoming aware of our breath, what we see, what we hear, and what we feel can quickly bring us back to our sensing mind and become aware once again of our now.

The easiest way to start shifting to the sensing mind is to focus on your breath and then move to what your senses are getting from your environment. Start with basic questions, such as: what do I see? What do I hear? What do I feel? What do I smell? Keep in mind that you are trying to do this while not judging what your senses are picking up. You are just becoming aware of your environment and experience at this moment. This means that you have no negative emotions associated with what you are sensing. The more you do this the more your mind will be trained to be present. Of course, this does not mean that you are trying to shut out your thinking mind. It is probably going to try to keep chattering away and comment about whatever you are sensing. This is okay. If it starts chattering again, simply quiet the voice. Imagine the volume of the noise in your head getting smaller. Focus back on your breath or use one of the many techniques you'll learn in this book. It takes practice, but it's well worth it because most people live their lives in their thinking mind and don't even notice that they are missing out on life.

The exercises in this section will help you develop your awareness of your senses and develop your sensing mind. Being in this state is also referred to as having a "child's mind" because you will be facing your environment with curiosity and intrigue about your current experience. By practicing you bring your mind back to the present moment through your senses you take away power from the thinking mind which gives you a chance to consciously choose your thoughts, focus, and emotions because you're finally aware enough to remember that you have a choice.

THE 5 SENSES EXERCISE

The next exercise is called 5 senses and it is another simple exercise that you can do at any time to expand your mindfulness habits. You can do it in a couple of minutes or take longer depending how much time you have. What you simply do in this exercise is notice things that you are experiencing through your different senses. This is a great experience to bring you to the here and now of your present moment. Keep in mind that you are not judging anything that you are sensing you are just bringing them to your awareness.

- Notice five things that you can see.
- Look at your environment and bring your awareness to 5 things you can see. Try to pick things that are not obvious or things that

you normally would not be aware of.

- Notice four things that you can feel.
- The next step is to bring awareness of things that you are you are currently feeling. For example, the texture of your pants or your shirt. It can be the feeling of something on your hand or the feeling of the cool air that may be blowing on you.
- Notice three things you can hear.
- The next step is to take a moment to 3 things that you can hear. These things can be a car in the distance, the air conditioner, a bird in the back ground, or even a conversation.
- Notice two things you can smell.
- Next take a moment to become of aware of two things that you can smell. These can be things that you may not ordinarily notice. It can be the smell of a flower that is in bloom, a nearby restaurant, the smell of the food your coworker is eating, or the perfume someone is wearing. Keep in mind that the smells do not have to necessarily be pleasant.
- Notice one thing you can taste.
- Lastly bring your awareness of one thing you can taste. This can be something that you are drinking, a candy that you may have in your mouth, or just notice the current taste in your mouth. You can even notice if the air has a taste when you breathe in.

MINDFUL SEEING EXERCISE

Mindful seeing is a simple yet powerful activity, especially for those that feel that they want the visual stimulus. Keep in mind that for some, using their imagination may not come naturally when meditating. Therefore, this is a great activity for those that identify with that. This activity is one that be done in a few minutes. The best part of the exercise is that it can be done anywhere that you have a view outside. Below are the steps:

- Find a space outside or looking out of a window, where you have a view of the outside world.
- Without judgement or labeling, look at what is in the environment you're observing. If you see a bird do not just label it as a bird, instead look at the colors, patterns, and the details.
- Look at what you are viewing as if it was new to you. In other words,

pay attention to the different shapes, to the wind and the movement of the grass or leaves, and all the small things, as if you were exploring a new reality. Make sure that you are aware of your environment but you're not fixated on just one thing.

- When or if you get distracted, gently bring yourself back to your current awareness of what you are seeing. In other words, choose a color or shape to refocus yourself. Remember not to judge yourself if your mind gets distracted.

 ## CANDLE MEDITATION

Using a candle's flame as a visual object of your attention for meditation is a practice that has been used throughout human history. You can complete this exercise using a real candle, placed 1 to 2 feet in front of you, or using the video we make available at https://www.transformationacademy.com/mindfulnessbook.

This meditation is as simple as sitting in a comfortable position in a dimly lit room and focusing both your sight and your attention on the flame of the candle.

- Take a few long, deep breaths and bring your attention to the flame. Watch the flame as it dances and observe the details of its movements.

- Look at the very top of the flame and notice that it is a different color than the bottom of the flame. Observe the smoke stream that leaves the top of the flame and billows up into the air. Observe if any wax is melting and watch it as it moves.

- When your mind wanders, gently bring your awareness back to the flame. You can do the activity for as long or as short as you wish, however we recommend at least 10 minutes.

You can enhance the experience of this exercise by assigning meaning to the flame.

For example, the flame is a wonderful metaphor for love and light. If you have been experiencing darkness in your life, as you observe the flame visualize the light penetrating the darkness of your mind. Allow the light and love of the flame to fill every cell of your body.

The flame is also purifying, and you can imagine the flame burning away any thoughts or feelings you may have of fear, hate, insecurity, anger, anxiety, self-judgment, sadness, guilt, or resentment. Imagine the light filling the space that was formerly taken up by the unwanted feelings.

You can also imagine that you are the flame and that you feel each movement that it makes, as well as it's heat. Allow the light and heat to fill your body and feel the joy of gentle movement.

And lastly, you can imagine that the flame is igniting your passions from within. Feel the excitement as you feel yourself expanding out into the world and becoming all that you were meant to be. Allow the flame to be the spark that ignites your destiny.

DAY 3: BODY AWARENESS

Our bodies are amazing machines that are alive and in constant motion. At any moment, even when we are still, there are sensations that can be felt within the body that are a great focus for mindfulness.

We will start by bringing our awareness to our bodies as a way of becoming mindful. Next, you will find a progressive relaxation meditation that will walk you through relaxing your body from head to toe.

 BODY AWARENESS MEDITATION

- For this simple exercise, you can be sitting or lying down with eyes closed.

- The first step to become aware of the body is to enter using the breath. Take a deep breath and notice the sensations within your body. Continue to breathe naturally. Notice how the air feels in your nostrils or mouth, how your chest or belly rises or falls with your breath.

- Your body is covered with your skin, which is an organ that is covered with sense receptors. Tune in to your outer body and notice anything you can feel. Notice the pressure where your body rests against the surface you are sitting or lying on. Notice the texture of the clothing you are wearing, where it is tight and where it is loose. Notice if any of your exposed skin can feel the gentle motions of the air. Is it warm or cool?

- Now, bring your attention to your inner body. Pay close attention and you may be able to feel or even hear subtle movement from within the body, such as your digestion, air moving in and out of your lungs, or the pulse of your blood circulating.

- Put your right hand over your chest and feel your heart beating. Now move your hand to your neck and you will feel your heart beating even more noticeably. Notice how the skin on your hand feels the touch of the skin of your neck as well as the sensation of the heartbeat. Also notice that the skin on your neck feels the sensation of being touched.

- Return your hand to a resting position. Now, bring your attention to the energy or life force that animates your body. Can you feel a warm or tingling sensation in your hands? Your face? Your chest? Your legs? Try feeling the sensation of the energy in your whole body all at once. It feels warm, alive, almost as if you have a current of electricity pulsing through your entire body.

- As you rest, gently aware of this powerful energy that you are, express gratitude for your amazing body and the intelligence that animates it. Acknowledge how wonderful it is that your heart beats, your lungs take in and release air, your digestive system extracts nourishment, and all of the other systems of your body continue keeping you alive in any moment, all without you needing to be consciously aware of it. You don't need to tell it to take a breath, circulate your blood, or heal a wound. It blesses you with this every moment of every day, for free!

- Take a deep breath and bring your attention back to the room you are in. For a moment, try to hold the awareness of your entire body AND the room around it at the same time. Take one more deep breath and come back to full awareness and open your eyes.

PROGRESSIVE RELAXATION

- Become aware of your breathing, and notice how your abdomen rises and falls with each breath...

- Mentally scan your body for areas of tension. Make note of how your body feels. During this relaxation session, you will focus on releasing any tension in your body and on quieting the mind.

- Now take a long slow deep breath in through your nose, all the way down into your stomach. Hold the breath for just a moment, and then exhale through your mouth. Allow your breath to carry away all stress and tension as the air floods out of your lungs.

- Imagine what relaxation feels like. It might feel warm...heavy or light... tingly... loose... relaxation is a pleasant, calm feeling... it feels very comfortable.

- Take another slow breath in through your nose. Fill your lungs completely. Hold it for a moment...and release the breath through your mouth. Empty your lungs completely.

- Take a third deep breath in. Hold it for a moment, and then let it go.

- The gentle rise and fall of your chest with each breath is so calming...so relaxing...each time you breathe out...and your chest lowers gently...you feel even more relaxed...

- Now let your breathing rhythm return to normal...and relax....

- During this relaxation you will tense various muscles throughout your body. Simply contract each muscle firmly but gently as you breathe in. If you feel uncomfortable at any time, you can simply relax and breathe normally.

- Bring your awareness to your feet and toes. Breathe in deeply through your nose, and as you do, gradually curl your toes down and tense the muscles in the soles of your feet. Hold your breath for just a few seconds and notice what that tension feels like. Now, release the muscles in your feet as you breathe out. Feel the tension in your feet wash away as you exhale. Notice how different your feet feel when tensed and when they are relaxed.

- Once again, draw in a deep breath...and tighten your calf muscles. Hold for a few seconds, and then let it all go. Feel yourself relaxing more and more deeply with each breath. Your whole body is becoming heavier, softer and more relaxed as each moment passes.

- Take another deep breath in... and tense your upper legs. You'll feel the muscles pulling your kneecap upwards. Hold for just a moment, and then release everything. As you do this, the blood flow to your muscles increases, and you may notice a warm tingling sensation. Enjoy this feeling of soothing relaxation.

- Draw in a nice deep breath and gradually tighten the muscles in your buttocks. Hold this contraction for a few seconds, and then release your breath. Feel the tension leaving your muscles. Feel them relaxing completely.

- Now bring your awareness to your abdomen and back. Draw in a nice deep breath and then tighten these muscles. Now release your breath and let your muscles relax. Notice the sensation of relief that comes from letting go.

- Now give your attention to your shoulder muscles and the muscles in your neck. As you slowly draw in a nice deep breath, pull your shoulders up towards your ears and squeeze these muscles firmly. Now breathe out completely and allow your contracted muscles to go loose and limp.

- Feel the heaviness in your body now. Enjoy the feeling. Feel yourself becoming heavier and heavier. Feel yourself becoming more and more deeply relaxed.

- You are calm, secure, at peace. Now it's time to let go of all the tension in your arms and hands. As you breathe in, raise your wrists towards your shoulders and tighten the muscles in your upper arms. Hold that breath and that contraction for just a moment...and then gently lower your arms and breathe all the way out. You may feel a warm, burning sensation in your muscles when you tighten them. Feel how relaxing it is to release that tightness and to breathe away all tension.

- Now, as you breathe in, curl your hands inwards and tighten the muscles in your forearms. Now feel the tension subside as you relax and breathe out.

- Now, take another breath in and tightly clench your fists. When you have finished breathing in, hold for just a few seconds, and then release. Notice any feelings of buzzing or throbbing. Your hands are becoming very soft and relaxed.

- Take a couple of nice long slow breaths now, and just relax. Feel yourself slipping even deeper into a state of complete rest.

- Now tighten the muscles in your face by squeezing your eyes shut and clenching your lips together. As you do, breathe in fully. Hold it...now breathe out and relax all your facial muscles. Feel your face softening.

- Notice how heavy your eyelids feel. Take another deep breath, and when you release your eye lids will feel heavier and heavier.

- You are now completely relaxed from the tips of your toes to the top of your head.

- Please take a few more minutes to rest. Relax. Listen to the sound of your breathing and enjoy the lovely, warm sensation of physical relaxation and sleep. You will awake feeling completely rejuvenated and relaxed.

Script by Christopher Lloyd Clarke from www.The-Guided-Meditation-Site.com.

DAY 4: MINDFUL EATING

Most of the time when we are eating, we are only partially aware of it. Sometimes we are rushing or distracted and don't even notice we are eating until we see that our plates are empty. This can be because we are talking, thinking, looking on our phones, or any number of reasons. In short, we are not mindful of what we are doing. And this is unfortunate because eating is a highly engaging, enjoyable experience! Sometimes we aren't even paying attention when we're eating the yummiest foods, and we miss out on the experience.

Eating is one of easiest and most enjoyable ways to practice being mindful, aware and present. You can practice mindful eating ANY time you eat by putting away the phone and removing other distractions and really focusing on every bite of your food. You can also deliberately choose a food you would like to experience fully, such as your favorite snack, and practice eating in full awareness.

Eating mindfully not only makes eating more enjoyable and helps you increase your mindfulness, it also helps you tune into your body so you can recognize when you're full and how your body reacts to the food that you eat, which helps lead to healthier eating habits.

Today decide either to choose a specific meal you will eat mindfully or choose a special food you would like to use for this practice.

- To eat mindfully is simple. Pay full attention to your utensil as you grab the food and move it toward your mouth.
- Pause for a moment just before the food enters your mouth and notice the sensations in your mouth as it prepares for the food, such as the sensation of it producing saliva. Notice if the food has a smell.
- As you take a bite, notice the feelings and sounds of the food entering your mouth and you begin to chew.
- Where in your mouth does the food move?
- What does it taste like?
- When you swallow, follow the sensation of the food as it moves down your throat.
- Take another bite and continue to observe the experience. After a few bites, check in with yourself to see if you can feel the effect of what you have eaten in your stomach.

- Throughout the meal, when you notice that your mind wanders, bring your attention back to the process and experience of eating. Savor every bite, enjoy the experience of it, and appreciate the nourishment that you are receiving.

MINDFUL CURIOSITY (USING THE SENSES)

In the following activity, you're going to use all of your senses in order to explore your curiosity about an item.

You will need a small piece of food for this exercise. Something with an unusual texture, smell, and/or taste is best. A raisin is commonly used.

Once you have your raisin or other food item, for the rest of the activity imagine that you are seeing one of these for the very first time. You're going to use all of your senses.

1. **Sight:** Start by holding the raisin between your fingers or in the palm of your hand and look at it closely, from all angels, as if you have insatiable curiosity about it. Observe the texture, color, size, and any other detail you notice.

2. **Touch:** Squeeze the raisin between your fingers. Notice how it reacts to the pressure. Rub your finger along the raisin and observe how it feels. Is it rough? Smooth?

3. **Sound:** Does it make any noise as you move it around or squeeze it? As you smell, chew, and swallow the raisin in the next steps, pay attention to any sounds that the process of eating makes.

4. **Smell:** Bring the raisin close to your nose and observe the smell. How does it smell? What does it remind you of? How does the smell make you feel?

5. **Taste:** Next, put the raisin on your tongue. Without chewing it, move it around in your mouth and observe how it feels on your tongue and what it tastes like. Notice how your mouth reacts by creating saliva to digest the food. Then, chew the raisin and observe in what way it feels or tastes different. Notice how your teeth grind the raisin and prepare it for digestion. Then swallow the raisin and observe how it feels as your throat contracts and it travels down your esophagus to your stomach.

DAY 5: MINDFUL LISTENING

MINDFUL NOISE

There is noise going on all around us all of the time. Sometimes the sounds can be pleasurable or soothing and other times it can be distracting or unpleasant.

- For this exercise, sit or lye in a comfortable position that will allow you to be completely still and free from distractions. Take a few deep breaths to center yourself in the moment.

- Pay attention to the sounds in your body. Sit or lay still and listen to see if you can experience any sounds going on inside of your body. Listen to the rise and fall of your breath.

- Now bring your attention to any sounds going on around you. First, notice anything close by, such as the sound of an air conditioner, refrigerator, or clock. Just witness the sounds without judging or labeling them. Then, bring your attention to more distant sounds. Perhaps the sound of the wind outside, a car driving by, or thunder in the distance.

- Shift your attention back and forth between the different sounds you hear, the distant ones, close ones, and then back to your body and breath. Cycle through them several times.

- Use whatever sound you are hearing at the moment to anchor you deeper and deeper into the present.

- Do this for anywhere from 5 to 20 minutes.

- You can also take a moment at any time to pay close attention to the sounds around you in order to bring your awareness back to the present moment, such as when you're sitting at your desk listening to the murmur of voices, sitting in your car listening to the hum of the wheels on the road, or lying in your bed hearing the crickets chirping.

However, sometimes noises can be irritating, like ringing phones, car horns, babies creaming, a particular person's voice.

These annoying stimuli can be a great opportunity to practice mindfulness. When you resist the sound, it's like your body stiffens and the vibration of the sound bounces off of you, beating you up. Instead, imagine your body is limp, like a noodle… imagine it is transparent and the sound can pass right through you. Notice how different this feels.

Pay fully attention to them. Go into them. Notice any rhythms. Imagine the noise is like a sound. Make up a beat or song that goes along with it. Imagine a funny cartoon scene going on along to the sounds.

By releasing your resistance to the disruptive sound you release your unpleasant reaction to it. Your curiosity overpowers your annoyance.

You can also use sound or music as a focal point for meditation.

MUSIC MEDITATION

You've already experienced the meditative effect of music any time you've gotten lost in a song. This happens because music helps stimulate reward pathways in the brain that are linked to positive emotions. You can use the music to boost your mood. Actually, there are specific types of music that have been shown through research to create relaxation and a sense of peace. These include classical, native American, Celtic, stringed instruments, drums, and flutes. But, music is also strongly associated with memories, which is why listening to a song you heard during a painful breakup will bring you down or a song you used to listen to in high school can bring you back. It's important to consider what music that you expose yourself to because depending on the type of music and the association you have with it, it will either alleviate stress or create more of it.

There are many benefits to using music as a point of focus and a mediation tool, including how easy it is to play a song any time, anywhere, even when you only have a few minutes to practice being mindful. Music can help with stress management by lifting your mood and slowing your breathing. Music has even been shown to impact your overall health. In fact, there are have been several studies that have demonstrated the benefits of music, including a study by a researcher named Novotney in 2013 that it showed that listening to music reduces levels of the stress hormone cortisol and another one by a researcher named Clarke in 2017 that music increases the body's production of the antibody immunoglobulin A which attacks invading viruses and boosts the immune system's effectiveness.

Now that you know how and why music can boost your mood and be a good mindfulness tool, let's explore a simple exercise.

The longer you can extend this process, the more beneficial it will be, however listening for the duration of a single song will be enough to help reduce stress and feel re-centered.

- Choose a song that you know will help you relax or put you in the state of mind that you are seeking to experience. You can create a playlist for longer sessions, or you can put one song on repeat.
- Sit in a comfortable position and close your eyes. Take a deep breath and relax your shoulders, arms, face, abdomen and legs.
- Now, focus on the music. Notice the rhythm, the tones and the rise and fall of the volume.
- If you catch your mind wandering, congratulate yourself for noticing and bring your attention back to the song.
- Notice any sensations you feel in your body in response to the song.

If you find that the song brings up memories, you may want to choose a different song.

DAY 6: MINDFUL WALKING

Walking has been shown to be one of the most important things we can do for our health, so establishing a routine of taking walks is a great idea. With the current trend of people using Fitbits or phone apps to count their steps, many people are already trying to get 10,000 steps a day. You might even be one of them! But this isn't about the physical benefits of walking, it's about the opportunity that walking offers for practicing mindfulness.

As with any other mindfulness activity, you can create a formal walking program, such as taking a walk at the same time every day. Doing it consistently and intentionally will greatly enhance the benefits you experience. But, the good news is that walking happens all the time, so ANY time you are walking is a good time to be mindful!

- Whether you're walking up the stairs, taking a walk in a park, or walking down a city street, don't just make your walking a means of getting from point A to point B. Be mindful of the experience so that you can actually experience it, rather than be lost in thought the whole time.
- With each step, notice the rise and fall of your feet and how it feels when your feet make contact with the ground. Notice how your arms sway with the rhythm.
- Notice your breathing. Is it fast or slow? Shallow or deep?

- When your mind wanders or something else captures your attention, bring your attention back to your steps.

- If you need help staying focused, count your steps from 1 to 10 and then back down 10 to 1 and repeat. This is also a great technique for moments when you go for a walk to clear your mind or calm down a negative emotion or obsessive thoughts.

- After paying attention to your steps and your breathing for a minute or two, shift your attention to your surroundings. What is going on around you? If you're in nature, what plants or animals do you see? Is there a breeze? How is the weather? Rather than labeling objects you observe or judging situations, just simply observe that they are there. If you're in a city, what types of buildings, vehicles, or people are around you? Again, observe them without judging or thinking about them.

- After observing your environment, bring your attention to how your senses are interacting with the environment. Are there any smells? Sounds? Changes in light? Other sensations?

- For the remainder of your walk, alternate your attention back and forth between your steps, your breathing, and your environment.

- When your walk is coming to a close, spend the last minute fully aware of the physical sensation of walking.

- When you are done walking, stand still for a moment. Pause to notice how it feels to be still.

DAY 7: MINDFUL DRIVING

Many people spend a lot of time on the road and in their car.

Have you ever driven to your job or your house and you didn't realize you were driving until you arrived? If so, you were on autopilot, doing the motions of driving using your unconscious mind while your conscious mind was off in La La Land. The truth is that driving becomes automatic and doesn't require our full attention, unless we're in traffic, and so most of the time our attention is mostly on whatever is going on in our minds, rather than on the road.

This mindful driving exercise not only helps you be more present while you're driving, which is great for your safety, but it is also a great use of your time. If you're going to have to be driving for 10 or 20 or 60 minutes, you might as well do something during that time that serves a purpose—like practicing your mindfulness!

Now, there are many productive things you could do while you drive, such as listen to audiobooks or online courses—in fact, that is something we have done for years and it has transformed our lives. However, we've also spent a lot of time on the road traveling far distances and spent hours at a time simply sitting in silence. Many people think it is pretty weird to travel with someone and not talk or even listen to music, however we enjoyed watching the landscapes out the window sitting in stillness.

And that's exactly what mindful driving is. It's about being acutely aware of your environment while you're on the road. It's a great way to practice honing your attention, plus it makes driving enjoyable—even during traffic!

Here is how to do it.

- First, when you get into your car, pay attention to how you have to shift your body around to get into the seat.
- Pay attention to the steps you take to buckle your seatbelt and start the car. Sit for a minute before driving away and just notice the space inside of the car.
- Notice the smell.
- Notice the different materials that make up the windshield, dashboard, steering wheel, display, and seats.
- Then, as you begin driving, pay close attention to every move you are making and how your movements gently guide the car.
- Notice everything that you pass, whether trees or people, signs or cars, buildings or the sky.
- If you stop at a red light, notice the stillness of the vehicles that are stopped and the relative speed of those that are passing by. Observe the glow of the light as it changes.

Stay in this state for 5 minutes, or longer if you desire. Then, you can do whatever you would normally do in the car (except texting… please, no texting!). For instance, you can put on music, and then while you're listening practice keeping all of your attention on the music (and of course, on the road). This way, you can practice your mindful listening at the same time.

WEEK 2: AWARENESS OF THOUGHTS AND EMOTIONS

DAY 8: THE PSYCHOLOGY OF THE MONKEY MIND

The truth is life is challenging. There will always be disruptive changes, conflict, disappointment, frustration, and loss. Life will push us out of our comfort zone, we will have to make hard choices, and terrible things will happen at some point. We will do our best to deal with it all, but the truth is that most people do not handle life all that well. They don't consciously evaluate how best to proceed and deliberately create better circumstances. Instead they have knee-jerk reactions to what happens around them. They get locked into automatic responses and negative habits. Their thoughts, emotions and behaviors are on autopilot. They aren't aware of the fact that they have a choice—that if they were more aware of what was going on INSIDE of their mind and how their thoughts were responding to the stresses of life—that they would eliminate a great deal of their suffering.

You see, it's not that the challenges of life are what cause us problems—the majority of our negative experiences are caused by having an untrained human brain. The most important reason to be more mindful is to combat dysfunctional, negative, compulsive thinking and the resulting stress and negative emotions. But we're not trying to make our minds the enemy here, we're trying to help you understand your mind better so that you can minimize your stress and unnecessary emotional suffering.

Mindfulness will help you master your monkey mind. The Buddhists called that chattering, negative internal voice that exists in our minds when we are not in a state of awareness of the monkey mind. The monkey mind is in a state of mindlessness, which is the opposite of mindfulness. But the good news is that when we get good at observing the monkey mind, we can take away its power to disrupt our life. So, let's get to know this monkey mind better by looking at some of the reasons we think the way we do.

Negativity bias—assuming the worst was a matter of survival when one small mistake could cost you your life. Our ancestors learned to assume the worst-case scenario as a way of protecting themselves. For example, if they heard a rustle in the bushes their mind would assume that it may be something trying to eat them, which would trigger their body to go into fight or flight mode. Even if they were wrong 99% of times it was worth it because that one time that they minimized it could have cost them their life. Therefore, our brain specifically the amygdala focuses on the negative so that we can minimize pain. Our brains are hard-wired to avoid anything that is painful and seek what brings us joy. Anything in the middle is forgotten. However, in today's society where we don't have the constant threat of life and death it is easy for our fight or flight to always be activated by minor stressors. Also, it makes it easy for us to be sucked into what we call in psychology the Hedonistic treadmill where we confuse the constant search for external things that make us feel good as happiness.

In other words, stress is hard-wired: We expect negativity but try to get away from it. This creates a conflict within ourselves. By becoming aware of our tendency to think negatively, we can choose a different way of thinking about situations that reminds us that we do not have anything real to fear—there is no sabretooth tiger hiding in the bushes—and so we can relax.

Desire for certainty—Another aspect is that our brains are created to seek certainty, resist change, refuse to see things for what they are, our cortex evolved to analyze our past & evaluate our future. That means that even when change will be positive for us, we continue to do the same things that hold us back because we are familiar with them. However, once we are aware of this tendency for our brains to try to sabotage positive changes, we can choose to override our instincts and commit to the life changes we're wanting to make.

Confirmation bias—this is another powerful aspect of our brain function. What confirmation bias does is that it influences our perception to see and experience what we believe to be true. In other words you can have two people experience the same things and yet have a totally different experience. Therefore, our perception of something influences what we experience and our memory of it. For example, if you think today is going to be a bad day your mind will try to highlight every negative thing to help you affirm that it is a bad day. Your mind is basically helping you affirm your belief system. This is one reason why mindfulness is so powerful because it allows us to see things for what they are, not from a biased perspective of what we think it should mean.

Belonging—Another aspect is that we have a natural need to conform to society and those around us because we are social creatures. This was part of our survival mechanism to work within a group. However, in today's society we create a preoccupation with self, comparison with others and the need to be accepted by others which can push us away from following our purpose and living a life that is truly in alignment with us. By becoming mindful of our influences and how we relate to other people, we regain our power over our decisions.

Understanding our monkey mind is essential to being able to create true, lasting change. Through the mindfulness techniques that you are learning you will be better able to manage your thoughts, where you spend your energy, and your ability to determine your own destiny.

MINDFULNESS OF THOUGHTS (AND HOW THEY CREATE EMOTIONS)

When you experience anything in life, it is interpreted by your brain, which means in a split second your brain compares what it is taking in through your senses, which tells it what is going on in your experience, to everything else you've ever experienced. It's trying to make a snap judgment of:

1. What is going on?
2. What does it mean?
3. How should I feel about it?
4. What should I do?

The brain has evolved to rapidly interpret everything you experience and it's so good at it that you don't even notice it's happening. That is, until something happens that causes your mind to interpret a situation as negative. It chooses a perspective or belief about the situation that creates an emotional reaction in your body. It's unpleasant, so it's noticeable. Your body reacts to this emotion, which is actually caused by the thought triggering your body to release any of a number of brain chemicals, often referred to as neurotransmitters or endorphins or hormones. Your brain is like a chemical factory and there is a different neurotransmitter that is responsible for every emotion you can feel.

It all functions as it should. Something threatens you, your brain interprets, triggers the hormones that shoot throughout your body inspiring you to spring into action. Someone tells you they adore you and you're flooded with feel-good chemicals. Our bodies and brain are amazing machines. But sometimes, these emotional reactions get out of whack with what's actually happening. You can feel anxious for no reason. Something small makes you furious. You're sad even when you're doing something that usually makes you happy.

What's happened is that your mind has learned a pattern of thinking that is faulty. Your brain is interpreting situations negatively, when they're not. Your mind is judging situations, or yourself. You have unconscious limiting beliefs impacting your perspective that you aren't aware of. Your brain was doing what it does best—trying to interpret your world in a way that protects you. Unfortunately, as you lived life, your brain got programmed by the world around you. Your thoughts were influenced by the actions of others. Your core beliefs were adopted from the beliefs of others. And because you weren't aware of any of this, your mind became trapped by its own faulty beliefs. Your thoughts run amok and you were never taught how to catch them.

It happens to everyone. Humans bodies and brains don't come with an owners' manual! But the good news is that the solution is simple. You can become more aware of this process. You can change your thought patterns and beliefs. You can reprogram yourself. You can become conscious of your unconscious thoughts and behaviors. You can choose to experience more positive emotions, and less negative ones.

You have this power to control your own mind—a power that has been withheld from you your entire life. And it's time to take your power back!

Let's Look at Emotions

The best place to start a discussion about how thinking works and impacts your life is to look at emotions. Let me ask you a question, should emotions be trusted?

Some people say, "You should always trust your emotions."

Other people say, "Feelings are irrational and can't be trusted."

So, which is it? They're BOTH wrong.

Emotions and feelings are neither right nor wrong, accurate or not. Emotions are simply your body's reaction to what you are THINKING. Your belief system and other unconscious thoughts are happening on autopilot all the time, and cause emotions. That's why sometimes you have NO IDEA why you feel the way you do.

Here's an example of why emotions are never either right or wrong... because they're just reacting to your thoughts...

- Think about something that you really, really wish you had, but that you don't have. You may feel unhappy because you don't have it, but that's not true. You are unhappy because of the THOUGHT of not having it.
- Let me prove it to you: Have you ever been happy while not having it?
- If you didn't have it but didn't care about it, would you be unhappy?
- If you didn't have it but were doing something that kept you from thinking about it, such as going down a roller coaster, would you be unhappy about it? No.
- You see, not having want doesn't make you feel bad. Thinking about it does.

Where Do Emotions Come From?

Sometimes our unconscious mind and senses are picking up cues from our environment that trigger emotions, such as reading a person's body language or facial expression and having an automatic physiological response or sensing danger and having an automatic fear response.

However, most of the time it is NOT the outside world or the situation that is happening that causes our emotional reaction—it's what we're thinking. It is the mental filter that the situation passes through—aka, our inference or interpretation—that then causes our emotional reaction to the situation.

Situation (activating event) → Inference (automatic thought) → Emotion

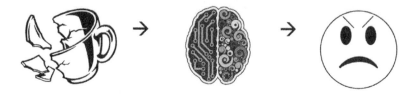

The key to understand here is that research over decades provides evidence that we can have control over our thoughts. And if we have control over our thoughts, we can control our emotions. It may be challenging to do this, but it is a skill that can be learned. Here's the process:

Recognize Emotion→ Identify Thought → Change Thought → Change Emotion

Changing the Thought

Once you notice that a thought is happening it becomes conscious. Since you're aware of it, you can then choose to change it. Your mind automatically interpreted the situation, but now that you're paying attention to it you can choose a different interpretation—a different perspective. This is great news because when you change the way you look at things, the things you look at change. Even in the same situation or with the same facts, if you change your viewpoint, your experience of the situation will change. Here is an example: a man was visiting a friend's house and went into the kitchen to make some tea. He didn't find a tea kettle, and so poured water into a glass coffee carafe and placed it on the gas stove. He returned to the living room and minute later smelled something burning. He returned and found that the handle of the carafe had caught fire. He quickly put the fire out. He apologized to his friend and was feeling both embarrassed and guilty. His friend, however, was laughing and complemented him on his "fireman" skills. Same situation, different perspectives—and the result was completely different emotional responses.

Why this matters!

This matters because, of course, you want to feel better. If you change your perspective of a situation, you will change your emotional reaction to it. But, it's even better than that!

You see, your emotions are the driving force for your BEHAVIORS because the decisions you make are based on how you feel. As you get better at being aware of your emotions and thinking, you'll be able to make decisions from a place of control—you might feel a certain way, but you'll use your cognitive processes to choose to act from a place of rational thought.

But, if you're like most people, you're not at that place yet—at least not all the time.

So, here's where we are now:

Thought → Emotion → Decisions → Action

The behaviors you exhibit and the actions you take are a direct result of your thoughts. So, if you are experiencing behaviors you don't like or have been doing things you aren't pleased with, your thoughts are to blame.

If you can't yet see the behaviors or actions you're doing that aren't serving you, look around at your life at the results you're experiencing. Have you been having any problems at work or in your relationships? Have you experienced anything unpleasant? Are there are things you want that you don't have? On the positive side, what aspects of your life have you managed to create that you want, enjoy, or love?

The reason we ask is because we're going to take this cause and effect train one more step.

That's right, your behaviors and actions are what determine the results and outcomes you experience in your life—both the wanted ones and the unwanted ones.

Thought → Emotion → Decisions → Action → Results

By changing your thoughts, you can literally transform your life. Literally! So, let's dive into more about understanding how thinking works.

OBSERVING YOUR TRAIN OF THOUGHT

Sometimes your thoughts are directly related to what is currently happening, whether it be the task you're working on at your job, the turn you're making in the car, or the food you're cooking in the kitchen. But, most of the time your mind is thinking about something ELSE. It's rehashing the argument you had yesterday, remembering that time in college you embarrassed yourself, judging the neighbor for their ridiculous holiday decorations, or worrying about your upcoming interview.

And these random thoughts have a strong tendency to be negative. This is why many people who study mindfulness or personal development say that they want to stop their negative thinking. Unfortunately, the truth is that you can't stop thinking, even if it's negative. Thinking happens all the time.

Once it's there, you can't simply stop thinking about something negative. In fact, trying to NOT think about something actually increases the likelihood you will think about it. It's a psychological phenomenon called Ironic Process Theory. Try it now. Do NOT think about a pink elephant. We forbid it! What's popping into your mind right now? A pink elephant. The same thing happens with your thoughts.

You can't stop thinking and you can't exactly control your thoughts, but you can get better at managing or directing them. The key to developing better control of your thinking is to practice observing your thoughts.

Thoughts come and go, like trains in a train station. Sometimes they move fast, other times slow. Sometimes they quickly pass through the station and other times you jump on board and get carried away by the train of thought until it gets derailed. And once one passes, there is another one right behind it. Sometimes they're negative, sometimes positive. Our minds are like our very own Grand Central Station with new trains of thought coming and going around the clock. It can become stressful and overwhelming when we don't know how to take a step back and slow down the activity.

The good news is that you have a choice regarding which trains you get on. If you were sitting at a train station would you simply hop on board whatever train came first? No, you would decide where you want to go and then wait for a train that is headed in the direction you want to go. But, unfortunately with our thoughts, we tend to think we are obligated to ride every train that enters our mind. And the more negative and unpleasant the thought is the more tempting it is to get on board.

All trains pass. If you find yourself on a negative one you don't like, you can't simply jump off. But, you can try to jump from that train to another one that passes by. From wherever you are, find the best thought train you can and keep focusing on that one. With practice you'll be able to break the habit of taking every thought train seriously and navigating your mind more deliberately.

It all starts with the simple practice of observing your thoughts. Mindfulness and meditation are tools for slowing thoughts enough that we can use them more deliberately. You can even widen the gap between your thoughts—those moments of stillness that happen when you find yourself in awe of a magnificent sunset or lost in the moment during a significant experience like a childbirth or the flow of your favorite activity.

Here's a simple technique to help you visualize the meditation process:

Mindfulness meditation is the practice of sitting in that train station in your mind and watching the trains of thought come and go. You're not getting onto any of them — you're making a conscious decision to let them pass.

Here's the step-by-step:
- A train of thought comes in
- Identify it ("I notice I'm having the thought that…")
- Now watch it leave, without engaging it
- Repeat for every thought that enters your mind (for as long as you can stand)

What this does, over time, is to help you to detach from your thoughts, so you don't just get on that first train that comes your way. Or, if you do find that you've gotten on board (and you inevitably will, often), then you recognize it, and get off at the nearest exit. This can be just as challenging as not engaging the thought in the first place, and detaching from a train of thought mid-transit is just as good of a skill to develop, so don't be discouraged when your mind wanders. This just gives you another opportunity to practice disengagement.

Detaching from certain thoughts is difficult, especially for things are triggering for you. But the more you make this practice a part of your routine, the more control you will gain over the contents of your mind, and the easier it will be to let unproductive trains of thought pass.

DAY 9: SORTING THOUGHTS INTO BOXES EXERCISE

SORTING BOX ACTIVITY

A great activity for creating awareness and differentiating between thoughts, emotions, and sensation is the "sorting into boxes" activity. This activity can be done in collaboration with any breathing activity that relaxes the body or the body scan activity. Many people find that their mind may wander into thoughts and by being able to separate them and identify them we separate ourselves from the thought and avoid personalizing them. It will also help your mind learn how to focus on the present moment instead of focusing on past or future. Below are the steps to doing this activity.

1. Get into a comfortable position and place a timer with a bell for at least 5 minutes
2. Focus on your breathing without attempting to change it.
3. As you find yourself in this relaxed state notice any thoughts, sensations, or feelings that may come up.
4. Every time something comes up imagine placing them in one of three boxes in your mind. Imagine these three boxes each labeled: thoughts, sensations, and emotions.
5. Do not judge the thoughts, sensations, or emotions as you continue to focus on your breathing. Your only role is to be able to identify them and place them in the appropriate boxes when they do come up.
6. Continue the process of clearing what comes up until the timer goes off.

URGE MANAGEMENT (URGE SURFING)

This mindfulness technique was originally created by professor Alan Marlatt for addiction treatment. The idea is that urges come and go much like waves. When we feel an urge, whether it's to eat a food that is not on our diet, yell at someone who has upset us, or take an action we know will have an undesirable outcome, we have two choices: give into the urge or resist it. But, the problem with this is that just like a wave, it is there whether we like it or not. When we resist it—when we struggle, we sink. We are taken over by the wave. This is why stopping a habit is so challenging. We don't realize that resisting it is not any better than giving into the urge. In many cases, resisting the urge makes it WORSE.

What's the solution? To keep calm and ride the wave! Surf the urge!

Here's how it works. Instead of trying to resist the inevitable wave by getting away from it, we're going to go deeper into it. By observing it more closely we take away its power over it. We watch the wave rather than getting swept up in it.

- Identify the location of the urge. Where is the urge originating from? Where in your body do you feel it? For instance, if the urge is to eat a piece of candy the urge may be impacting your tongue, making your mouth water. If the urge is to hit someone who angered you, the urge may originate in your gut or perhaps your heart area. Once you've identified where it is coming to, bring your attention to the details. What sensations do you feel? Are there any feelings of warmth, pressure, tingling, energy, discomfort? Get as detailed as possible. In fact, if you are having a hard time not giving into the urge, add complexity to this step. Describe the sensations out loud. Use examples or a metaphor to explain it. Move your body as you describe it. By keeping your attention on the fact that it is simply an experience you are having, not who you ARE, it takes away its power over you.

- Shift your attention to your breath. After you've identified the specific sensations of your urge, shift your attention to your breath. Notice how your breathing is correlated with your urge. Is your breathing fast or slow? Shallow or deep? Through your nose or mouth?

- Shift your attention back to your urge. Notice how shifting your attention influences the experience of your urge, as if it changes the magnitude or size of the wave. Switch your attention back to your breath for 5 seconds and then back again to the urge. Notice again any difference.

- Anticipate the fall of the wave. All waves rise and fall, and your urge will fall as well. As you continue to observe how your urge feels, anticipate the inevitable reduction of the wave. You will notice the peak pass and the wave begin to fall, and with it relief from the feeling of the urge.

DAY 10: AWARENESS OF SELF-TALK

There are two layers of thoughts—the ones we can hear or experience as the voice in our head, that makes commentary about ourselves and everything around us, and the deeper level beliefs that determine our opinions, perspectives, and judgments.

Our self-talk can be an inner cheerleader that motivates and sooths, or it can be an inner critic that is harsh and self-defeating. Our self-talk impacts how we feel about ourselves as well as how we behave and is ultimately responsible for our experience of life and the outcomes that occur because of our actions.

For instance, you may have heard of the concept of a self-fulfilling prophecy, which is a psychological concept that basically means that we will live up to our own expectations or create the situations we expect. For instance, if you are constantly telling yourself you're a failure, it impacts the way you feel—discouraged, self-doubt, anxiety—which impacts how you act and the choices you make. Either you'll make poor choices, like deciding not to try, or when you do take actions, you'll give half-hearted effort. Why bother? You're going to fail anyway, right? In the end, you fail. But it's not because you're a failure, it's because of your thinking.

The deeper level beliefs you hold about yourself, others, the world are what causes your inner voice to talk to you, about you, the way it does. One important thing to know is that you were not born with either a cheerleader voice or a critic voice—you learned how to think this way. How? By observing the way your caretakers and others talked about themselves, about others, and about you. You weren't born fearing failure. When you were a toddler you made a mistake and just kept right on going, that is, until an adult acted like falling down was the end of the world or shamed you for doing something "wrong". Over time, that external voice becomes your internal voice. If you're a parent, think honestly for a second about what you have programmed your child's inner voice to say to them. Ouch.

If you just realized that you have programmed some limiting and harsh self-talk into your children, and you're realizing that you've probably been programmed this way too, there is good news. WE CAN ALL BE REPROGRAMMED.

By becoming aware of your self-talk, the positive and the negative, you can CHANGE IT. Self-talk is simply a habit of thinking. Start out by considering the general predisposition of your inner voice. What percentage of the time do you think your inner voice falls into these 3 categories:

1. Criticize yourself, put yourself down, talk negatively to yourself.
2. Make excuses, blame others, tell yourself it's not your fault
3. Tell yourself it will be okay, encourage yourself to learn from the situation

There is nothing right or wrong about your answer to this. Everyone has an inner cheerleader and an inner critic, however the vast majority of people have a very dominant inner critic. This negative side of your thinking can present itself in a variety of ways, which we'll get into in a moment. This is like the fixed mindset persona, but in its full form.

Before we move on, we want to make sure that you always remember that your inner critic is NOT you. Take a moment and give it a name (you can use the same name you created for your fixed mindset persona). We like to call ours "Bob"!

Negative Self-Talk Triggers

There are 4 common and easy-to-spot ways that your inner critic shines it's light of negativity on your world. Try to catch it in the act. When you notice it thinking one of these types of negative thoughts, simply observe it. Don't judge it or criticize it because if you do, it's just the same inner critic voice coming in the back door again. Think about that one—now you have 2 Bobs! Yikes!

1. **Self-limiting.** When my Bob is trying to limit me, he says things like "it's too hard, I can't do this" or "it's too risky" or "I don't have time". Ultimately, Bob likes making excuses. This is even more common if you lean toward having a fixed mindset, like

we discussed already. When you believe your abilities are fixed and you believe failing means you are a failure, the best way to avoid humiliation is to not try at all—which is what excuses are for, aren't they? Your Bob tries to shut down possibilities and solutions before you even get started.

2. **Assumptions.** Bob's believe they're always right and that they're psychic. They like to think they can read other people's minds and assume what they're thinking and feeling. They like to jump to conclusions and make snap judgments. The Fact or Opinion activity is great if your Bob likes to assume things. Look out for your Bob saying things like "everyone will talk about me", "I made a fool out of myself", "she doesn't like me". Your inner critic is making up stories that aren't even true. Once you know this, you won't fall for it so easily.

3. **Re-runs.** Most of our self-talk happens on autopilot. Our repetitive, automatic thoughts have been going on for so long we don't even notice them. Chances are your Bob says things all the time that you don't even actually believe, but you let him get away with it because you're so used it. Often these habits of thought become habits of speech, so you may even catch yourself saying these things to others, out loud. Be on the lookout for 2 things:

4. **Thoughts,** especially memories or anticipated events, that tend to replay a scene in your mind over and over again, like a mini-movie on re-run.

5. **Phrases** you say to yourself or others repeatedly, especially if they are making a judgement about yourself.

   For example: "I'm always late" or "I'm an idiot" or "here we go again" or "this always happens to me".

6. **Others' Thoughts.** Sometimes your Bob is simply parroting someone else. You will be shocked when you realize how many of the thoughts that go through your mind are NOT your own. It is time to GET OTHER PEOPLE OUT OF YOUR HEAD. Like we already mentioned, your inner dialog has been programmed throughout your life. Your nagging mom now takes up residence in your mind. The good news is you can kick her out! The key for this one is to question the thoughts you have about what you

"should" or "shouldn't" do. These words are a sign that the belief behind them was planted by someone else. If YOU actually believed it, in most cases you wouldn't be telling yourself you SHOULD do it, you'd just simply do it.

- Ask yourself, "Who's voice am I hearing?"
- Do I really believe that I "should" do this? (Hint, if you're feeling a sense of guilt, it's probably not your own, original, belief.)
- If yes, make it a MUST and do it.
- If not—if this is someone else hijacking your mind, tell them to GET OUT and then ask yourself, what do I really believe?

What's Your Inner Critic's Personality?

You've named your inner critic so you don't take it so personally and you've learned what to look out for in order to get good at noticing your negative thinking. Now, let's look at 4 common personality types that your inner critic may have. Understanding the way your inner critic tends to think will help you identify what you can do to tame it.

- **The Worrier:** Points out everything that can go wrong. Stirs up emotions of anxiety and fear by imagining disasters, expecting the worst, and overestimating the odds of something bad happening. It tends to say, "what if"?
- **The Critic:** Constantly judges and evaluates your behavior and points out your flaws. Jumps on any mistake you make and reminds you of past failures. Compares you to others and assumes they will judge you. It even minimizes your accomplishments! It tends to say, "you're an idiot".
- **The Victim:** It tells you that you're hopeless, not making progress, or that it's too hard. It tells you there is something wrong with you, your incapable, unworthy. You're not smart enough. There are too many obstacles in your way. It's not your fault. It tends to say, "I can't."
- **The Perfectionist:** It pushes you to do better but even when you do better you still feel like you're not good enough. There is always more you should be doing. Mistakes and setbacks must be avoided or quickly moved past. It pushes you to seek external validation, achievement, status. Acceptance by others is

of the utmost importance. It probably even stops you from taking action because you're afraid to fail. It tends to say, "I need to do better" or "I'm not good enough".

Take Your Power Back from Bob

Now that you know what to look out for so you can notice your inner critic in action, go out into the world and practice observing it. When you catch your Bob in the act, use the following 3 strategies to take your power back from these negative thoughts.

- **Ignore Bob:** Don't take Bob seriously. When Bob starts rambling on incessantly or hops on a negative train, imagine Bob has a funny voice or is wearing a clown suit. Bob is not you, and it doesn't know what it's talking about.

- **Protect Bob:** Bob's easily influenced, so always ask yourself if YOU really believe what it's saying. We already talked about getting people out of your head. One way to do this is pay special attention for any thoughts coming from Bob that sound eerily similar to things other people say (such as your parents, the media, authority figures). Choose what you expose Bob to wisely, because he's apt to believe it and repeat it.

- **Observe Bob:** As often as you can, remind yourself to watch your Bob. Notice what it's thinking about. If you don't like what it's thinking about, CHOOSE A NEW THOUGHT. You're in charge. Many of the activities discussed throughout this book are designed to help you observe, record, and re-direct your Bob.

Remember that it takes time to get good at keeping your Bob in check. You'll notice times when Bob runs off on a tangent of terrible thoughts without you noticing—sneaky Bob! But no worries because when you eventually notice what Bob is doing you can WHACK Bob on the head—it's like playing Whack-a-Mole. Whack him and say, "bad Bob!" and laugh. This stops the negative thought, giving you a moment to remember that you have a choice. You can then implement one of the thought-changing strategies you learn in the book and pick a better thought. The more you observe your Bob the better you'll get at catching it in the act—and as you practice, the voice will get quieter and your inner cheerleader will take the lead.

DAY 11: DEVELOPING EMOTIONAL AWARENESS

Sometimes people have a difficult time identifying their emotions and it's usually because of one of the following reasons:

- We were made to think our feelings don't matter
- We were made to fear expressing our emotions
- We were made to feel guilty if our emotions (or desires) were an inconvenience on others
- We were discouraged from feeling or expressing specific emotions

Because of our conditioning, some people stop expressing their emotions and often repress them (hold them in). Other people go a step further and stop allowing themselves to have them. In either case, this can lead to a lessened ability to recognize how they feel.

Even people who did not learn to repress or turn off certain emotions—even if they feel things deeply—they can simply not have ever been taught about their emotions and so they cannot clearly identify them. Their emotions feel overwhelming and out-of-control.

If you want to re-gain your power to direct your own emotional state, you need to be able to:

- Notice you're experiencing an emotional state
- Identify what it is
- Know what to expect
- Know how to influence a new emotional state

Emotional States

Emotional States are actually 2 different things:

- The STATE is the physiological "feelings" that you experience
- The EMOTION is the psychological interpretation or "label" you put on the state

We experience complex states made up of chemical and hormone interactions that cause a variety of reactions in the body. Our emotions are the interpretations we make of these experiences—or the labels we give them.

Based on what we talked about in Thoughts Create Emotions, we need to add a couple steps to the process.

Situation → Interpretation (thought) → State → Interpretation (label) → Emotion

What this means is the body responds to the thought first, then our minds interpret the reaction, label it, and an emotion is born.

We can have physiological feelings that aren't emotions. We can feel hot, cold, nauseous, or energetic. But, when we interpret them to have meaning, we turn them into emotions.

Emotions literally mean action: e-MOTION. Each emotional state is designed to get us to do something, and often we do. Our emotional state affects our behavior, but it does not cause it. When we're angry we're more likely to be aggressive, but our cognitive (thought) processes allow us to make those decisions.

The Map is Not the Territory

The labels we give emotions are like a box or a map. What's printed on the box may signal what's inside, but it is NOT what is inside. Just like a map may describe a territory, however it is NOT the territory. Maps are simplified, inadequate and ultimately flawed. It would be like eating a menu. In the same way, what we call "anger", the word, is not the experience. Saying you "love" someone hardly does the experience any justice. In fact, all words are simply signposts pointing toward meaning. The word "tree" is not a tree.

So, what IS an emotion if it's not a map? Well, it's not a "thing" either. You see, labeling an experience as an emotion makes it seem like a NOUN. This is why many people believe emotions are things they HAVE or that happen TO them. The truth is that emotions are verbs (emoting is the verb)—they are a PROCESS. Fear is the process of fearing, which is a string of sensations that occur in a pattern. Fear takes many steps from observation or contemplation to processing and interpreting; then to physiological reaction and FEELING, and finally labeling it as fear.

If you obscure the process underneath a word label, you end up believing that emotions aren't under your conscious control. Once we recognize anger is a process, we recognize we have power over it.

Emotion Identification Chart:

On the next page are 6 common emotions and descriptions of the emotion, physiological state, and common resulting behaviors. This chart will help you get a general idea of the signs and symptoms of each emotion to make them easier to identify; specifically, easier to identify early. Keep in mind everyone experiences each emotion somewhat differently and you may not experience all of the characteristics.

See next page.

LABEL	EMOTION	STATE	BEHAVIOR
Happiness	Intense, positive feelings of well-being, pleasure, contentment, delight, joy, optimism, and gratitude. Affirmative, positive thoughts and mental clarity.	Head held high (posture), wide-eyed, smiling, laughing, relaxation of muscles, open body language.	Pleasant voice, friendly, swinging arms, dancing.
Boredom	Low-intensity, unpleasant feelings of apathy, restlessness, indifference, emptiness, and frustration. Defeatist thinking or wishing things were different.	Low energy, slumped posture, smirk or frown, low eyes, shallow breathing.	Resting head, fidgeting, staring.
Anxiety	Vague, unpleasant feelings of distress, uneasiness, stress, apprehension, and nervousness. Thoughts of uncertainty and worry, racing thoughts, difficulty concentrating and remembering.	Restlessness, sweating, clammy hands, hunched shoulders, swallowing, quickened breath, darting eyes, butterflies in the stomach, nausea.	Pacing, biting lip, fidgeting. Irritability, hypervigilance.
Anger	Intense, uncomfortable feelings of hostility and hurt. Feeling out of control. Thoughts of blame and resentment. Difficulty thinking clearly or rationally.	Muscle tension, headache, tight chest, increased heart rate, increased blood pressure, heavy breathing, clenched fist, furrowed brow, showing teeth, clenched jaw, sweating, trembling, flushed cheeks, large posture.	Loud voice, yelling, cursing, sarcasm, pacing. Sometimes leads to aggression, including hitting a wall, throwing an object, or lashing out at a person.

Sadness/ Depression	Feelings of intense pain and sorrow, guilt, unworthiness, disappointment, helplessness, gloominess, loss, grief, numbness, meaninglessness, loss of interest. Defeated thinking and difficulty concentrating and remembering. *(Depression is a long-term period of sadness that is caused by more than a psychological reaction to circumstances. Depression is a real and serious condition and needs to be treated by a medical professional.)*	Slumped posture and hunched shoulders, long face, slow movements, pouting, body aches, crying, shaking, crossed arms, fatigue, upset stomach, monotone voice.	Curling up into a ball, laying around, withdrawing, irritability.
Fear	Intense feeling of dread, impending doom, or panic due to a perceived danger or threat. Paranoid or worst-case thinking and hyper focused on the object of the fear.	Increased heart rate, increased blood pressure, alert eyes, high eyebrows, corners of cheeks pulled toward ears, clammy, sweating, quickened breath, goose bumps, butterflies in the stomach, shaky voice.	Freezing, fleeing, hiding.

Practicing Emotional Awareness and Identification

Next time you catch yourself experiencing an emotion that is distinct, ask yourself the following questions. Practice this line of questioning often, especially when experiencing unpleasant emotions.

- How do I feel?
- How do I know?
- What do I feel? Sensations?
- Where do I feel it? Locations?
- Where in my body did it begin? Move to?
- How do I recognize when OTHERS experience this emotion?
- Do I notice any of these signs in myself?
- What do I observe in my body language, vocal tone, thoughts, behaviors?

RAIN TECHNIQUE FOR ACCEPTING EMOTIONS

The four steps of rain are:

1. **R** Recognize what is happening
2. **A** Allow life to be just as it is
3. **I** Investigate your inner experience
4. **N** Non-Identification

R = Recognize. The first step is to recognize that you are experiencing an emotion and you're your thoughts, emotions, and behaviors are impacting you. All emotions can have mental, emotional, physical, and behavioral symptoms, and you may notice one symptom before the others. For example, you may first become aware of an inner critical voice, or you may first feel the physical symptoms of fear or anxiety. You also may become aware that you are yelling or shutting down. When you first become aware of the emotion, remind yourself not to judge it. Emotions are natural, healthy, and normal. The purpose of this activity is to develop a better understanding of it. First, give the emotion a name. Doing this helps you separate the emotion from your identity. For example, "I am feeling stressed."

A = Allow or Accept. The second step is to be able to allow the emotion to be there without trying to stop it, fix it, or label it as bad. But, keep in mind that accepting the reality of your experience does not mean that you like it or want to keep it the same. This just means that you are not repressing your emotion or resisting what IS. Instead of trying to avoid it, you are shining light on it. This is an important step because when we try to deny what is, whether it is the situation that is upsetting us or the emotion we are feeling, we cause more suffering. Our resistance adds another layer of stress. If we deny ourselves the emotions and repress it, it goes on to eat away at us from within where it will fester and create worse emotional and physical pain and disease in the long term. By allowing the emotion to be there we stay focused in the present moment which is where we are able to process and then release the emotion. By facing it we take back our power to create long term change. For example, weeks and months after my (Joeel) brother died, I found myself having moments where I felt severe sadness and instead of hiding it from myself I would go to a private space and allow it to be there and I would cry, and I would feel a weight lifted after the fact. This allowing helped me not to be in that space and allowed me to release the emotion.

I = Investigate. In the third step you would take time to investigate the feeling and the emotion. In other words, call on your natural curiosity without judging the situation. So, you are not trying to necessarily fix anything you are just trying to develop an understanding of how you feel and why. For example, you can ask yourself:

- How would I describe the emotion I am feeling? What sensations do I feel in my body?
- What thoughts are going on in my mind?
- Have I felt this way before? And if yes, when?
- Is there a trigger or events that made me feel this way?
- Do I need anything in this current moment?
- Is my thinking realistic? Do I have the full picture about this situation?
- What does this feeling want from me?
- Is there a factor that may be affecting my emotions, such as not getting enough sleep?
- Are there things I could do to nurture myself?
- Am I exhibiting any behaviors because of how I feel?
- What are the consequences of acting out on this emotion?
- How will accepting and releasing this emotion positively impact me?

N: Non-identification. The last step is to accept that the feeling, thoughts, and emotions are not you. You are the awareness that experiences the emotions, but you are not the emotions. They do not define you. By recognizing that your thoughts, emotions, and behaviors are not who you are, you are better able to observe yourself and see that the experience is temporary. Your awareness gives you the ability to be the observer and allow the emotion to pass, and it also gives you the opportunity to make a decision about how you wish to respond.

DAY 12: MINDFULNESS FOR ANGER AND OTHER NEGATIVE EMOTIONS

MINDFULNESS FOR ANGER

Becoming aware of our emotions is the first step. The next step is to develop the ability to manage them.

Anger is one of most challenging emotions and can be destructive to our wellbeing, our relationships with others, and even our bodies. Anger builds in intensity the longer we hold onto it, so the key to managing anger is to defuse it before it builds and leads to negative consequences. Often, anger comes on rather quickly due to a trigger and the resulting impulsive response. By practicing mindfulness with your anger, you can learn to lengthen the space between the trigger and the response.

All emotions are felt physically, but anger is especially distinct and easy to identify in the body, making it an ideal emotion to practice emotional awareness with. This activity will help you practice identifying emotions in your body and then using mindfulness to reduce the emotional response to the trigger.

Let's begin:

- Sit in a comfortable position, close your eyes and become aware of how your body feels in the chair. Then bring your attention to your bodily sensations.
- Take several deep breaths, when doing this make sure that you are completely filling up your lungs and quickly exhaling.
- Now, remember a time where you experienced mild anger or frustration. Allow yourself to feel that anger for a few seconds.

- Now focus on how your body experiences this emotion. Are there any parts of your body where you tension? Heat? What sensations do you feel in your chest? Hands? Abdomen? What facial expression do you have? Is your heart rate impacted? How are you breathing?

- Everyone experiences anger differently, but there are many common physiological responses, like a furrowed brow, grinding teeth, clenched hands, rapid heart rate, rapid breathing, and tension in various parts of the body.

- Remind yourself that anger is a natural emotion that everyone feels from time to time. place your hand over your heart and be compassionate with yourself. Remind yourself that even though you have a completely valid reason for being upset that you do not have to suffer with this emotion of anger.

- Then release your anger. Imagine the tension in your body releasing. Relax the muscles and clear out the other physical sensations. Allow the anger to leave your body, as if you're letting it float away in a river. Imagine waving goodbye to it.

- Bring your attention to your breath and consciously slow your breathing, gently watching it move in through your nose and out through your mouth. Watch as your body calms down and the sensations diminish.

- After this practice exercise, reflect on the experience. What sensations did you experience end how did they change through the process? How did bringing compassion to your anger impact your experience?

- Once you have practiced this several times and you can clearly observe that the process of releasing the anger is working, you can move from mild forms of frustration or anger to more intense anger. Every time you practice this you will exercise your emotional control muscle and your ability to defuse anger or other emotions will continue to improve.

- You can also practice this using other emotions, like anxiety, sadness, guilt, etc. Not only will you become more mindful of how your emotions react in your body, you will more quickly be able to identify the emotions when they occur in everyday life and release the sensations that hold them in your body. With time you will be able to prevent them from escalating and will experience a sense of greater emotional control and wellbeing.

WILLING HANDS

When the mind is having a hard time accepting something, emotionally we tend to feel frustration or anger and the body reacts by tensing up. Because of the connection between the physiological reaction in the body and the underlying thoughts and emotions, if we change the state our body is in we can impact the emotion.

During times of resistance or anger, we tend to clench our hands. So by unclenching and deliberately relaxing our hands, which we refer to as willing hands, we signal to our minds that we want to accept reality. Even if the situation is something you are not okay with, it does not help you to remain in a state of tension and resistance. By releasing the tension and being in an accepting state, you will feel better and think more clearly about the situation, which is the only way you will be able to effectively deal with it.

- You can practice now by remembering a conflict you had with someone recently that made you angry.
- Clench your hands in anger as you remember how this situation felt. Hold this for a few moments until you can really feel it.
- Then, release the grasp, relax your fingers, and fully open your palms as if you are releasing the anger and tension and accepting the situation.
- If you're standing, with your elbows bent, open your hands turning them palms up.
- If you're sitting, place your hands on your thighs with palms up.
- If you're lying, place your arms by your side with palms up.

By practicing this willing hands position you are signaling to your mind that you're not longer resisting this. As your acceptance increases your anger will decrease.

Practice this several times using different situations that have made you angry. Then, as you go about your daily life, the next time you feel tension, resistance, or anger, remember to unclench your hands and then open them into the willing hands position to help lower your resistance and release your anger.

DAY 13: INTENTIONALLY CREATING DESIRED EMOTIONS

Now that you've practiced identifying, observing and shifting your emotions, it's time to take it to another level and intentionally create the emotions that you want to experience. Like we've discussed, emotions are not something that simply happen TO us. They are caused by our thinking, whether we are judging what is currently happening or thinking about the past or future. We've talked about how we can shift our thinking in order to change how we feel. But, we can also decide how we WANT to feel and deliberately practice those emotions.

Often, we believe that something has to be different for us to feel good. We tend to tell ourselves "I'll be happy when…" We'll finally feel at peace and relaxed when this test is over. We'll finally be happy once we are on that vacation. But the truth is that even once those conditions we wait for finally come, we probably won't feel the way we want. Why? Because we might go on that vacation but instead of being mindful and observing the beauty around us and taking in every moment, our minds will be lost in thought about the argument we had with our boss before we left or the massive workload that we will be coming back to when we return.

Putting off our happiness to some future moment that may never come can lead to massive disappointment. But even more importantly, it gives away our power. By saying "I'll be happy when" we're ultimately saying that we cannot have the emotional experience we want until this, that, or the other thing happen. There is a CONDITION that must exist for us to feel the way we want. Have you ever heard of the term "unconditional love"? Well, conditional love would be only loving someone if certain criteria are met. Unconditional love means loving them no matter what. Loving someone unconditionally doesn't mean you would simply accept being treated terribly, it means that even if they treated you terribly you would still love them and value who they are—even if you decided to draw clear boundaries or end the relationship.

But, that's a whole other topic. The point is that all emotions can either be conditional or unconditional. You can either tell yourself that you can only feel happiness IF certain criteria are met or you can tell yourself your happiness is unconditional. You are not going to wait to feel happy, you're going to choose to feel it now.

And that is the truth. You CAN choose to feel any emotion that you want to right now. Sometimes you just don't want to. Sometimes you would rather try to control a situation (even though you can't) than feel good. Sometimes you want to believe you have to be unhappy until something happens because if you could be happy without it you think it would mean you don't value it or want it as much. Sometimes you want to have something to complain about because if you didn't what would you talk to your friends about?

The reasons we choose to feel bad are beyond the scope of this book, but it is important to recognize that the truth is that we DO have a choice. We have the ability to feel the way we want *without* needing any of the conditions.

And, so, if you want to feel better, to feel good, to be happy, you can practice the feelings you want to experience with these simple exercises. And the great news is that when you practice feeling positive emotions your brain releases the endorphins into your body that make you feel good. And the more feel-good chemicals in your body, the more receptors your new cells create that are capable of absorbing those feel-good chemicals. You can literally train your body to feel better!

Method 1: Imagining the Desired Outcome

Think of a dream or desire that you have for your future. This would be some condition you want because, ultimately, you believe it will make you feel a certain way. Once you identify what this dream is, ask yourself what emotion you expect to experience when this dream happens. It's important to notice that the REAL reason you want this dream is because of how you will FEEL about the outcome. Anyway, once you identify how you want to FEEL you can give yourself a shortcut to the experience. You can imagine yourself living your dream NOW, including feeling all of the emotional benefits.

You see, your brain doesn't know the difference between imagination and real life. So, all you have to do to experience that glorious emotion you want to experience is to IMAGINE yourself living this dream. Close your eyes and imagine yourself acting it out in real life. What would it look like? What would you be doing? What are you wearing? Who is there with you? Are there smells in the air? Sensations in your body? Go there now. How would you feel? Make it as real as possible. Imagine yourself feeling that emotion you desire. How good does it feel that this is happening?

You'll find you can feel the emotion just by pretending it's happening. And now you do not have to use the fact that your dream has not come true yet as an excuse to feel bad or put off being happy.

Method 2: The Cultivation Circle

Just like you cultivate a garden by planting the seeds you want and feeding them what they need (light, nutrient rich soil, water and your attention), you can cultivate emotions. In the last method, you were thinking about a dream that you have that you want to enjoy. The visualization works because when you think about this dream it makes you feel good. But, sometimes the emotion you want to feel is actually because you are wanting to STOP feeling bad about something. This topic is not like the dream. When you think about it, it doesn't make you feel good.

For example, if you were worried about an upcoming family gathering when you were going to have to spend time with your mom, whom you have a really rocky relationship with, thinking about the upcoming event would probably make you anxious. Sure, you could try to remind yourself of the positive experiences you have had with her. You could focus on all of the other people who will be there that you will enjoy being around. You could even strategize ways to make the experience with her better by avoiding the topics that tend to trigger your arguments.

All of those things would help you feel a little better, but they won't make you feel the way you really want. How you WANT to feel is confident going to the family gathering. You want to feel at peace with yourself, centered, and confident knowing you can maintain your own calm and enjoy yourself even if your mom tries to bring you down.

And so, why not take it BEYOND just trying to find a way to feel better ABOUT the upcoming situation. Why not stop thinking about the topic entirely! Why not just focus on feeling the way you WANT—confident and peaceful?

Any time you want to feel a certain way, whether it's because you're wanting to feel better about something or you simply want to experience a particular feeling, use this Cultivation Circle exercise to help you create the desired emotion.

The Cultivation Circle

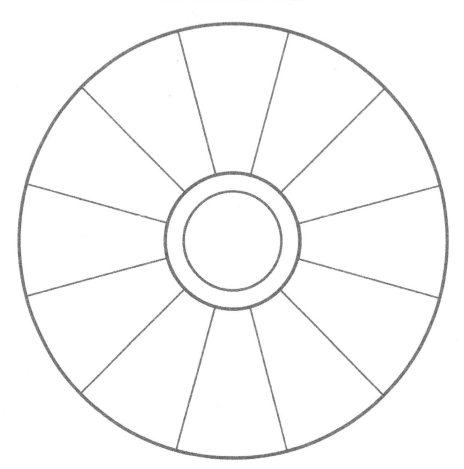

Draw a small circle in the center of a piece of paper and write the emotion you would like to cultivate in the center of it. You may also use the circle provided.

Around the circle, write as many things as you can think of that make you feel that way. At least 10. For instance, if you want to feel happy and carefree, you could put down: playing with my cat. Watching the sun set. That time I went on a road trip with my best friend. The way I felt the other day when I found a $20 bill on the sidewalk. The point is to identify ANYTHING that makes you feel that way, even if it is small. The easier it is to think about these things and feel good the better.

Notice that the topics you are using to cultivate the emotion do not have to have ANYTHING to do with the reason you want to feel that way.

For instance, with the example about wanting to feel confident and peaceful about the upcoming family gathering, you do NOT put "confident and peaceful about mom" in the center of your cultivation circle, you simply put "confident and peaceful". And, when you're doing the activity, you do not want to include anything directly related to the upcoming event. Just put things in general that make you feel confident or peaceful. You simply want to practice feeling those emotions. In the case of practicing the emotion you want to feel to counteract a negative feeling, like in the family gathering example, after you have done 3 to 5 cultivation circles practicing the desired emotion itself, you can hold onto that feeling and then practice the imagination exercise. Imagine yourself feeling confident and at peace arriving at the event, greeting family members, and giving your mom a hug. Imagine feeling confident, knowing that you have now practiced this desired feeling and can find your way back to it easily. Feel at peace knowing she does not have the ability to force you to feel bad and that you can always take a moment to re-focus yourself and make a cultivation circle in the bathroom if you need to.

THE HALF-SMILE TECHNIQUE

Now let's look at an uplifting mindfulness exercise called the Half-Smile Technique

The mind doesn't know the difference between what we're thinking and what is happening in real life, and so it responds by creating an emotional response to our thoughts. The same thing happens with our bodies. When we move our bodies in certain ways, such as smiling, the brain interprets our movements and responds. In this case, when we smile, our brain thinks we must be happy, and so it literally produces happy chemicals. This is called facial feedback. It's so effective, in fact, that call centers have put mirrors up for their operators to seek while they're on the phone, an they're asked to smile at themselves because it has been proven that doing so increases customer service ratings, as well as telemarketing sales.

This simple activity takes advantage of this ability to trick our brains into feeling good—or at least feeling better—and it has been used to treat a number of mood disorders—in fact studies have found it is even more effective than antidepressants! *(That being said, keep in mind that depression is a medical condition. Techniques such as the ones discussed in this book may be effective for feelings of sadness, however depression is more than an emotion. Never stop taking antidepressants or other medications you have been prescribed by a doctor without guidance from your doctor.)*

Because the facial muscles are so responsive to our emotional states, when we change our facial expressions we can alter our emotions. This can be useful if you're in a negative emotional state. By relaxing your forehead, eyes, cheeks and mouth you can reduce your negative emotion. Then by adding in a half-smile you can help increase positive emotions. You can also use this technique anytime you want a quick boost!

First, let's practice adjusting our facial muscles. Try to make your face completely neutral with no expression. Relax your forehead, eyes, cheeks and mouth. Notice how this feels.

Now, begin to smile by lifting the corners of your lips, but stop just when you start to notice a little tension at the corners of your mouth. If someone was watching you, they probably wouldn't even notice that you're smiling. It's subtle but you can feel it. There is no added benefit smiling really big, and in fact it can make your face get sore during the exercise.

Now, hold your smile for 5 to 10 minutes.

You can enhance the benefits by smiling with your eyes too, focusing on the feeling of happiness, or even doing your mindfulness meditation while holding the smile.

The best thing about this exercise is that you can do it anywhere, any time, without anyone noticing, so give it a try the next time you're sitting in traffic or waiting in line.

Fake smiling is powerful and tricks your brain into thinking you're happy, but real smiling is even better! Do this quick experiment.

Imagine you're at a party that you do not want to be at. Put on a fake grin to make everyone think you're enjoying yourself. Notice how your face and emotions feel. Now think about something that genuinely makes you small or laugh, like your pet, a laughing baby, or your favorite funny movie. Evoke a genuine smile and notice the difference in how your face and emotions feel.

Even the fake smile is helpful, but as often as possible give yourself a super boost by thinking about something that will bring you a genuine smile or laugh. Why do you think funny cat videos are so popular on YouTube!? They make people smile.

THE POWER OF GRATITUDE

Gratitude has been shown through research to be a powerful tool to decrease negative emotions such as anxiety and stress among others. We cannot be in a state of gratitude and be angry, anxious, or depressed. Therefore, taking the time to focus our attention to what we are grateful for in our life we can shift our state. One of the best ways to shift our day is to start our day in a state of gratitude.

There are simple ways to be more mindful of the things you have in your life to be grateful for. For example, in the morning you can take 5 minutes to make a list of things that you are grateful for. Or, throughout your day keep a notebook and write things that you are grateful for as they come to you. It is important to remember that gratitude is not about being grateful for just the good things in your life, but it is also about being thankful for everything in your life. For example, it is also being grateful for situations and experiences that may initially seem bad, but with time they prove to be a blessing and an opportunity to learn and grow.

There are many different places you can look for something to be grateful for.

- Call in one big thing: A big change that transformed your life in some way or a challenge you overcame.
- People in your life: It can be a person that has made a big impact in your life or someone that did something minor like smiled at you that shifted your energy.
- Something simple: Such as the sunshine, your ability to walk or see, your coffee, that you have a job. These are easy to take for granted.

Keep in mind that these are just an example of things that you can be grateful for, but you may think of many more.

❁ GRATITUDE MEDITATION

- To begin, find a quiet place where you know you will not be disturbed.

- Sit upright in a comfortable, stable position where you feel fully supported, and your back, neck, and head are straight. Or lie down on your back in a comfortable place

- Allow your eyes to gently close.

- Take a slow, deep breath to bring yourself to the present moment and begin the process of feeling more peaceful and centered. Breathe into the belly so it expands as you breathe in and gets smaller as you breathe out.

- Now, mentally scan your body for any areas where there is tightness, tension, or soreness and breathe your warm, oxygen-filled breath into that area; as you breathe out, let the tension release, breathing it out.

- If you notice any thoughts or emotions, allow them to flow out as you breathe out.

- As we start the gratitude process, start by acknowledging that if you are listening to this meditation you have marvelous gifts.

  - The gift of hearing that allows you to hear these words, listen to beautiful music, and hear the voices of those you love, the song of a bird, the notes of a band or orchestra, the songs of singing and voices, the sound of your own breath flowing in and flowing out.

  - The gift of life itself, including your heart that beats and gives life to your body, the food that nourishes you, and the energy that you are.

- Now, think about all the things we have in your modern lives today that make our lives more comfortable and convenient than they for our great-grandparents' generation.

  - We flip a switch, and light appears.
  - We turn a tap and clean, drinkable water flows.
  - We adjust a thermostat, and a room grows warmer or cooler.
  - We have a roof to keep us dry when it rains, walls to keep out the cold wind, windows to let in the light, screens to keep out insects.
  - We enter a vehicle and it takes us where we want to go.

- We have access to machines that wash our clothes. And we have clothes to wear, places to store them.
- There are machines that store our food at just the right temperature and help us cook it without us having to gather wood.
- We have indoor plumbing.
- We have public schools that can teach us to read and write, skills that were available to only the very few just a few hundred years ago.
- We have connectivity and access to all of the knowledge that has ever existed in the history of the world through our smart devices.

- Now, take a moment to reflect on all the thousands of people who have worked hard, most without knowing you at all, to make your life easier or more pleasant.
  - Those who plant, grow, and harvest your food.
  - Those who transport that food to market.
  - Those who take the time to design the store, the shelves, the packaging that keeps the food safe and allows you to find what you need.
  - The postal workers who sort and deliver the mail.
  - Those who maintain the servers that allow the internet to be available to us anywhere and anytime.
  - Those who design operations and systems for gathering, sorting, and disposing of trash and recycling.
  - Those who gather news stories and photos, and those who create the many mechanisms by which the news of the events of the world can reach you.
  - All those who play sports, create art or music, or films to entertain and uplift you.
- Now, consider the people and pets you know who enrich your life, those who smile at you and cheer you on, those family, friends, acquaintances, colleagues, and peers, those ancestors who worked so you could live well, those friends who support you when you need a shoulder or a hand.
- Now, take a moment to reflect on your own reasons for feeling grateful in this moment. Choose one memory you are grateful for.

One current life situation you are grateful for. And one future possibility you are grateful for.

- There is so much to feel grateful for in this moment now [10 seconds]. Gratitude fills our hearts and minds, uplifting our spirit [10 seconds].

- Rest quietly for several minutes, noticing how you feel throughout your body, emotions, and thoughts compared with before you started. No judging, just noticing. Now, gently stretch your hands and arms, feet and legs. And open your eyes.

With practice, you can find yourself feeling grateful easily, wherever you are. Remember that gratitude doesn't have to be for dramatic life changing circumstances, it can be simple appreciation for the often-overlooked miracles of life.

Explore this and other meditation scripts at Greater Good in Action https://ggia.berkeley.edu.

DAY 14: SURRENDER: ACCEPTANCE, LETTING GO OF THOUGHTS AND WORRIES

Many people have a negative association with the word surrender because they think it means that they are giving up, giving in, or waving a white flag. Surrender does not mean to give up, it means to accept what IS. And people don't like this word "acceptance" either. They believe that to accept something means to say that it is okay or to approve of it. So, let's clear up these misunderstandings.

To accept something means to acknowledge the truth of it. You might not like it, you might not want it, but it IS. Only by being willing to look at the full truth or the reality of it can you deal with it. You see, the opposite of surrendering is RESISTING. When something is happening that we don't want, we tell ourselves, "this shouldn't be happening." We fight against reality. In that state we can't do anything about it other than sit there and feel helpless or angry because it "shouldn't" be. We might avoid the person we're having the trouble with. We might argue for something to be changed that cannot be changed. Because we are not willing to really look at reality and we continue to resist it, we are stuck.

Only when you accept the reality that it IS and you surrender to it can you see clear enough to know the best way to respond to it. Only then can you choose to let it go and find a place of peace, contentment, or even happiness EVEN THOUGH there are things going on that you don't like. You are no longer a victim of it.

By surrendering, you aren't giving away your power, you are taking it back.

For example, for people who find it difficult to meditate, the most powerful thing they can do is to stop trying to "do it right". Instead, if they just allow themselves to be present and observe their thoughts, feeling, and sensations they will find that they are accomplishing the goal of mindfulness and meditation without trying so hard. When they focus on what they think it SHOULD be like or judge themselves for not doing it right, it gets in the way of them experiencing it. By letting go of the need to DO meditation and trusting the process and knowing that they cannot do it wrong, they get past their resistance and allow it to unfold.

Surrendering to Emotions

Surrendering is like allowing yourself to approach the world with the same curiosity that you had as a child. It is accepting things for what they are, including your emotions. In other words, if you feel sadness or fear, surrendering means you observe it and learn from it instead of just trying to label it as good or bad or telling yourself you shouldn't feel that way.

It is important to remember that negative emotions are normal. It is 100% normal to have negative, limited, or even scary thoughts or emotions. It isn't because there is something wrong with you. It is because your brain is trying to protect you. It's also important to remember that all emotions and thoughts will eventually pass.

The reason this is so important is because if you resist your emotions, if you judge yourself, if you push against them you add another layer of negative thoughts and emotions on top of what you're already feeling, which only makes it worse.

Instead of judging your thoughts or emotions, simply observe them. Notice them. Allow them to be there. Be curious about it, rather than judging. Then, because you've let go of resistance for a moment, you may find yourself beginning to think more clearly. In that moment, you can remind yourself that you're normal. Everything is okay. This too shall pass. And, once you've accepted the emotion, THEN you can use some of the tools you've learned to shift your thoughts and emotions.

Practicing Acceptance and Surrender

The reality is that we have many things in our life that are outside of our control. Yet, we try to control the uncontrollable. We resist what is, and this resistance causes emotional distress.

You can't control other people or what happens, but you can control how you react to these things, even in extreme circumstances. For example, when I (Joeel) was sick, surrendering was my biggest lessons. There were times that my body would shake uncontrollably, my blood pressure would spike, and my heart rate would spike for no apparent reason. At the beginning I would judge it and try hard to control it even though I had little control. However, one day I decided I would surrender and instead focus on my body and gratitude. Therefore, as I laid there I took the time to say thank you to my body to my heart for allowing me to have one more day of life and that I am open to allowing my body to do what it felt it needed to without any resistance. This may not have changed my medical situation, but it changed my experience of it. It helped me let go of all fears, concerns, and my unfeasible expectations. In other words, it taught me how to just be.

Mediation and mindfulness teach us how to surrender and how to be in the present moment. They teach us how to feel an emotion or how to have a thought without placing judgement on it. It also allows us to be mindful of our world in the present moment as an observer without judging it which allows us to have the power to see things more clearly without bias. By becoming the observer of ourselves and our reaction to the people and circumstances of life, we are no longer simply reacting—we are consciously aware of our reaction to what is.

Of course, this does not mean that you just meditate your life away and not take actionable steps to reach your dreams. It means you use mindfulness and meditation to center yourself, calm your thoughts and emotions, and make peace with what is so. And then from that place of clarity you can find your way to feeling better and creating change.

🪷 RELEASE/SURRENDER MEDITATION

Identify something in your life that you feel resistance about. This may be something that you wish you could change but you cannot. Something you are having a hard time accepting. Or even something from your past that is negatively impacting your life.

Once you have identified what you would like to surrender in this session, ask yourself whether there is anything that you CAN do about this situation. For instance, can you communicate something to someone or take some form of action in the future? If so, when will you do it? By acknowledging what IS within your power and committing to do what you CAN, you reduce your resistance.

However, even if you will be able to influence this situation to some degree, you cannot resolve it right now. You also may not be able to resolve it fully because the circumstances are outside of your control. You may not be able to change it at all.

However, whatever aspects of this situation are outside of your control are what they are. You acknowledge now that resisting what is only creates suffering for yourself.

Repeat the following:

- I am willing now to stop trying to control the uncontrollable. I feel a sense of relief as I begin this release meditation with the intention to accept this situation as it is so that I can free myself from the burden of resistance.

- I am willing now to stop suffering. I acknowledge that my worry, frustration, or anger about this situation in no way impacts the situation or helps me in any way.

- I am willing now to surrender to this moment and be here fully, releasing any attachment to a belief or demand about how anything SHOULD be. I choose now to see this situation fully as it is and accept it in this moment.

Then, continue with this meditation exercise:

- Get yourself in a comfortable position either sitting or standing, and then close your eyes, take a deep breath and let out a deep sigh as you relax all of the muscles in your body. Take another deep breath and let out a long sigh while pushing all of the air from your lungs.

- Now, allow yourself to breathe normally and simply observe the gently rhythm of your breath. Allow your body to breathe freely, at its own pace. Let it be as it is.

- Now, bring to mind the circumstance that you have chosen to focus on for this exercise. Allow the thoughts about this circumstance to show up however they come to you. Just notice whatever memory or imagined future comes to mind. Notice any words or voices that accompany your thoughts. Notice any feelings you experience in your body, whether they are emotions or sensations. Do not judge the situation or yourself. Allow yourself to go into the memory or thoughts of this situation fully.

- If there are any parts of the story that you have been unwilling to look at, it is time to see it clearly now. Allow yourself to look at it, all of it, see it for what it is without condemning it. Simply acknowledge the Isness of it.

- Now, bring your attention to the emotions that you feel. Do not hide from them. Allow them to be. Acknowledge them for showing themselves honestly to you. Witness them.

- Is there any fear that comes up? Any frustration? Any anger? Any sadness?

- Continue to allow these emotions to come and go as they are, without judging them or trying to change them.

- Now, imagine yourself holding your arms up to the sky, with your palms open and facing up. (You can do this in your imagination or for added power, do the motions physically.)

- Imagine looking to the sky and allowing your fear to rise into the clouds.

- Say to yourself "I release these fears, one at a time, once and for all. I surrender and accept what is."

- Allow your arms to drop and place your hands over your heart.

- Now bring up the feelings of frustration.

- Now, imaging yourself holding your arms up to the sky, open your palms and allow the frustration to rise up into the clouds.

- Say to yourself "I release these frustrations, one at a time, once and for all. I surrender and accept what is."

- Relax… Allow your arms to drop and place your hands over your heart.

- Now, bring up the feelings of anger.

- Now, imaging yourself holding your arms up to the sky, clenching your fists.

- Take a deep breath and as you breathe out open your hands and allow the anger to rise up into the clouds.
- Say to yourself "I release and let go. I accept and surrender to what I can't change."
- Relax and bring your arms down and place your hands over your heart.
- Now, bring up the sadness. Image yourself holding your arms up to the sky, open your palms and say to yourself "I may feel sadness but that is ok. Being able to let go and fully surrendering gives me strength and freedom. Accepting what I can't change gives me power over my emotions." It gives me:
  - True Freedom
  - Freedom from my past
  - Freedom from the things that I can't control or change
  - Freedoms from my fears
  - Freedom from my frustrations
  - Freedoms from my anger
  - Freedom from my sadness
  - Freedom to have peace in my life
- I fully surrender and accept what is understanding that it is a sign of strength, not weakness.
- I surrender the negative emotions now and release them into the sky.
- I understand that those things that we cannot control can be our greatest teacher at times.
- I surrender, understanding that this is what is meant to be.
- I surrender, knowing that I have the choice to let go.
- I fully surrender and I am now at peace.
- Take a deep breath and allow yourself to feel the sensation of peace.
- Take another deep breath and come back fully to your mind and body
- Allow your eyes to open when they're ready.

WEEK 3: AWARENESS OF SELF AND WITH OTHERS

DAY 15: EVERYTHING WE EXPERIENCE IS INTERNAL

Human experience exists 100% internally. Everything you have experienced has happened inside of you, including your mental/emotional feelings and your senses of sight, sound, smell, taste, and touch.

What you see: You are truly never experiencing the physical world. Point your finger at what you are looking at right now. Where is what you are seeing? If you say, "where I am pointing" you are incorrect. Light is falling upon what you are looking at which then reflects and enters your body through the lens of your eye, where it is projected as an inverted image on your retina. Then, your brain interprets this image (and turns it the correct position) and identifies what you are looking at based on stored memories of previous experiences. What you are seeing is taking place within you. Depending on the material it is made of, different light waves are absorbed and others reflected off, giving it an appearance of different colors when the frequency is interpreted by your brain.

It is actually your past experiences (stored in a framework of memory and resulting beliefs), not the current object in front of you, that ultimately determine what you see. There is a hotly debated story about a native tribe that lived by the ocean who had never had visitors approach their land from the sea. A large ship was approaching the shore and the natives could not see the ship until their leader, who had noticed unusual wave patterns and intently observed to see where they were coming from, became aware of the ship and alerted his tribe. Now, he didn't know it was a "ship"—in fact there are many accounts of natives describing ships as floating houses or moving islands.

The story is debated because there is no historical recorded evidence and many argue that although they could not understand what they were seeing (interpretation) they could still physically SEE the ship. This, however, isn't necessarily true. Have you ever been looking for something, such as your keys or an item in the refrigerator, and you cannot find it, and then later you realize it was literally right in front of your face?

The truth is that, although we can usually see things that are "new" and simply not know what we are seeing, there are times when our references (beliefs) prevent us from seeing what is right in front of our face. This is exactly why magicians can trick us so easily.

Physical touch: If you pet a cat, you may think you are experiencing their fur or the vibration of their purr, but actually you are experiencing the sensation in your hand that you are only able to feel because your brain is interpreting the vibration of friction between you and the cat. Even more interestingly, at an atomic level, it is technically impossible to touch ANYTHING. Quantum physicists have taught us that the atoms we are made of are mostly empty space (which is a mind-boggling point for another time), with a compact neutron at the center and protons and electrons orbiting around it. The simplest way to explain it is that these particles operate much like magnets. Electrons are negatively charged and protons are positively charged. There are many more electrons than protons, and therefore the electrons in atoms repel the electrons in other atoms, and so 2 atoms never touch—they simply hover really, really close. This means the atoms in our hand never touch the atoms in the cat's fur.

Emotional experiences: External situations may stimulate you, but the source of your experience of it is within you. Whether you are feeling emotional pain or you're blissed out, the source of those emotions are chemicals produced within your own body. What you observe outside of you is interpreted by your brain, based on your beliefs and expectations, and then your brain responds by coming to a conclusion that then triggers chemicals to be released and signals to be sent throughout your body, causing you to feel emotions and have reactions to what you observe. It is not what happens in your life that makes you feel the way you do, it's the meaning you ascribe to the situation, which is determined by your framework of understanding, your beliefs, and your interpretation. And finally, your brain responds, and you "feel" the effects of the chemicals that are released into your body and your body's response.

It sounds a bit weird. We know. But this is how it works. And it's good news, because if your emotional and thought experiences are internally generated, this means you can create them intentionally. Your brain may automatically interpret what you take in from your senses and react physiologically, outside of your control. However, the thoughts you hold ABOUT what you take in through your senses, and the thoughts you think about that are NOT related to your immediate surroundings, and therefore the emotions you experience, ARE within your control.

SELF-INQUIRY MEDITATION

Self-realization first begins by realizing what we are not. Self-awareness is what gives us the ability to consciously respond to our environment, deliberately create our thoughts and emotions, and relate to and understand other people.

We're going to begin with a self-inquiry meditation that will explore the answer to the question, "Who am I?"

- Get in a comfortable sitting position. Take a few deep breaths and allow yourself to settle in and become centered.

- Now focus your attention into the inner feeling of being you. Ask yourself, who am I? Imagine this "I" being located in the center of your forehead. Ask yourself, how does it feel to be me? Allow any feelings, whether they're physical or emotional, to come into your awareness.

- After sitting with the feeling of being you for a few moments, bring your attention to the contents of your environment. For this part of the process you may open your eyes. Observe what you see in the space around you. The objects, the space, the beauty, the imperfection. Say to yourself, "this is not who I am." Followed by "So, who am I?" Just sit with whatever answer comes to your awareness in this moment. Become aware of the fact that as your external environment or life situations change constantly there is an "I". Ask, "Who am I?"

- Now, bring your attention to your sense organs. Notice what you hear, smell, feel, taste or see. Imagine your ability to see was dramatically impaired. Notice that the "I" that is the seer is not impacted by the change in your ability to see. Imagine your ability to hear was dramatically impaired. Notice that the "I" that is the hearer is not impacted by the change in your ability to hear. Ask, "Who am I?"

- Now, close your eyes and bring your awareness to your vital organs and bodily processes. Sense your heart beating, your digestion, and the complexity of the human machine that you are. Notice that whether your heart rate is fast or slow, your stomach is full or empty, or your machine is working in harmony or a state of disease, there is an "I" that exists beyond it all. An "I" that experiences life in this body but is not the body itself. Ask, "Who am I?"

- Bring your awareness to the thoughts in your mind. You may be hearing the words of this exercise in your mind, whether my voice or yours. You may have been experiencing intermittent random thoughts throughout this exercise. You may find yourself thinking about the sensations in your body related to what you were just considering. You may be hearing answers echoing in your mind to the question you asked, "Who am I?" Whatever thoughts may be in your mind now or at any moment, notice they are usually accompanied by words. Sometimes these thoughts move fast, other times slow. Sometimes they are positive, other times negative. Sometimes they are about your identity, your traits, or who you think you are. Other times they're about others or your opinions or judgments. Sometimes they are about what is happening in this moment and other times they are about memories or the potentials in the future. But more than anything, notice that regardless of the contents of your mind and thoughts, there is always and "I" who is there beyond the thoughts, an "I" that does not change depending on your thoughts. Ask, "Who am I?"

At the beginning of this exercise, you were asked to imagine that this "I" existed at the center of your forehead, however the truth is you are much broader than this. Ask yourself "Where am I?" and simply observe the thoughts or sensations that come as an answer. Feel that you inhabit it all… the mental space, the body, the senses, and even your environment… feel yourself filling your body and overflowing into the space around you. Be with all of those things but know that they are not what or who you are. Who you are is beneath, beyond and bigger than any of it. Feel the power and magnitude of who you really are.

DAY 16: SELF-COMPASSION EXERCISE

Many people find it easy to have compassion for others. They recognize others struggles, honor their needs, understand their concerns, and wish them well. But when it comes to how they view and treat themselves when they are experiencing similar life challenges, they do not extend that same kindness. It is common for people to judge themselves harshly, put undue pressure on themselves, and negate their own needs. But by learning to practice self-compassion, you can improve your well-being, confidence, and resilience. You deserve to be honored and acknowledged for your struggles and to be treated with loving kindness by yourself.

This simple self-compassion exercise will help remind you to acknowledge your pain and be kind to yourself. Any time you are feeling stressed, overwhelmed, or in pain, use the following process.

- Touch your heart with your hand or give yourself a hug.
- Take a few deep breaths.
- Acknowledge that you are suffering and treat yourself as you would a small child who was struggling.
- Offer yourself phrases of compassion, first by acknowledging your suffering. You can say, "This is painful" "I am suffering right now" or "This is really difficult" or "Suffering is part of being human"
- Then, finish the exercise with a final phrase that wishes yourself well. Here are several ideas—use whichever one fits the situation:
  - May I hold myself with compassion.
  - May I love and accept myself just as I am.
  - May I experience peace.
  - May I remember to treat myself with love and kindness.
  - May I open to my experience just as it is.

Then you can return to your daily activities while continuing to hold an attitude of self-compassion and acceptance throughout your day.

🪷 MINDFULNESS MOUNTAIN

- Sit comfortably and take a moment to center yourself. Ideally you will be sitting upright in a confident position, feeling supported and at ease in this position.

- Observe your breath, relax, and then expand your awareness to the sensations of your body. Notice the surface beneath you and how it supports you. Root your body to its strength.

- Visualize or imagine a grand mountain. It can be one you've seen or one you make up. It can stand alone or be part of a mountain range. This mountain has been here for a long time. It is supported by a vast foundation of bedrock and it is unmoving and powerful.

- It may have jagged ridges or smooth slopes. It can be tree covered or bare. Blanketed with snow or dripping with waterfalls.

- However it is, let it be as it is. Perfect.

- Be this mountain and experience its stillness.

- With your head at the peak and your spine as the axis, feel yourself become centered and grounded. Feel the core of the mountain that remains unchanged even as the seasons begin to change around it. (Pause...)

- Be the mountain as the season turns to autumn and you are surrounded by golden light and bright colors as the cycles of life shift toward decline. (Pause...)

- Watch as the dormancy and darkness of winter take hold and sustain through the intensity of the violent weather, ice, and snow. Notice how the mountain remains still, quiet, and steady through the storms. (Pause...)

- Feel the warmth of the sun as it begins to warm once again. The stirrings of new life immerging from the thawing ground. The rush of melt overflowing and cascading from the mountain's peaks. Hear the songs of birds and watch the wildflowers sprout in a dance of new beginnings. (Pause...)

- Bathe in the heat as summer ignites a furry of growth and life, as thunderstorms roll through your valleys.

- Watch as the sky becomes a-glow with deep orange and yellow as the sun sets behind you, slowly turning to darkness that reveals the galaxies and endless space beyond, only to be obscured again with the rosy hues of dawn.

- Be the mountain that remains still and grounded through the changes of the weather, time, and seasons that take place at its surface, undisturbed at your core. Notice how day and night come and go, the seasons are in a constant state of change, and yet you resist nothing, knowing that deep down you remain unchanged, secure, safe, and whole. You.

Like the mountain, your life will present an ever-changing experience at the surface and you will experience varying degrees of darkness, light, activity, and stillness. But always remember that at your core the truth of who you are remains strong and patient, allowing everything that passes to be as it is as you enjoy the variety and colors of life with composure and compassionate clarity.

DAY 17: THE IMPORTANCE OF CHOOSING INPUTS

We're social creatures by nature, which makes us heavily influenced by other people. And we have a natural drive to want to belong, meaning that we will conform to those that we deem important. We also are social learners, so we will pick up the habits and behaviors of others. Because of this, one important area of mindfulness is to be mindful of who we really are versus who we are being based on our influences. If we simply allow whatever and whoever is in our environment to influence us, we will just become a product of our environment, only becoming aware of who and what is influencing us and our decisions. If we develop the awareness to truly understand ourselves, then we can make a conscious decision about who we want to be and how we want to live our lives.

You've probably heard the phrase, "you are what you eat," and this is literally the truth because your body breaks down whatever you eat and converts it into the building blocks of life and forms all of the cells in your body.

However, what most people don't realize is that, in this same way, our social inputs, like the people, the culture and the media that we consume, are the inputs that act as the building blocks of how we think, feel, act, and ultimately our life experience. Let's look at how this works in more detail.

First, let's look at people. The people that you socialize with, especially if you're around them regularly, influence your opinions, your desires, and the actions that you take. That's why there's a common phrase, "you become the five people that you're around the most." You will tend to believe what they believe, desire what they desire and do what they do. If you're around people who value education, you're probably going to go to college, and if not, you probably won't. If you're around people who value partying and drug use, this is what you're going to gravitate towards. If you are around people who believe the only way to make a living is working at a job that you hate and getting paid less than you need, then you're likely to tolerate this. Yet, if you hang around entrepreneurs or people who love their careers, you will choose a different path for yourself.

Next, let's look at cultural influences. The people closest to us and those we look at as authority figures have the biggest influence over us, but our broader culture, our acquaintances and the media influence us, too. For example, our concept of beauty comes from whatever culture that we live in. In a country called Mauritania, obesity is seen as beautiful. In their eyes, obesity signifies wealth, which makes them sexy. Some women in Mauritania go through extraordinary measures to gain weight in order to feel sexy. In some cases, they go to the extent of force-feeding girls so that they can be as big as possible. This is in sharp contrast to the common expectation of thinness that is portrayed as beautiful in the Western world. Beauty is just one mental concept that is shared with members of a common culture. Religious views, familial expectations, gender roles, social interaction, and many other aspects of life are determined by the cultures in which we live. In most cases, people accept their cultural norms as a given and do not stop to question whether they, personally, agree with and wish to adopt the cultural norms.

And then, there's the media. The media that we expose ourselves to has just as big of an influence on us as our broader culture. The media reinforces cultural expectations, however it also provides variations of norms, so depending on which media you watch, you are influenced in a different direction. Media can include TV shows, movies, the news, online articles, print media, books, music, and of course social media. For example, in recent years, it's become more and more obvious that people's choice of news media dramatically influences their perspective of domestic and global policies and politics. Yet, their political and cultural perspectives influence which media they choose, and so they become trapped in a circle of self-reinforcing exposure, with the absence of any new or contrary information that might shed light on a perspective beyond their own.

Media also influences our moods. For example, whatever music that you listened to puts you in a certain mood. The content of the lyrics that you listen to influences what you think about or even what you believe. That's why we'll put on a song that gets us fired up when we want to boost our confidence or we'll put on a soothing song when we want to relax. The input, which is the music, creates the output, which is our mood.

And then, there's social media. There have been many studies about social media and the impact that these forms of media have on our actions and our beliefs. It has been found that the behaviors demonstrated by people we follow on social networks, such as Facebook, can predict what behaviors we will demonstrate. For example, if people in your Facebook feed are eating at restaurants a lot, then you typically are going to eat at restaurants more often. If they're consuming more alcohol, then you are more likely to start consuming more alcohol. And this happens because those around us help define what normal is, even if we're only seeing these people in digital world on social media.

The reason all of this is important is because all of the inputs we're exposed to, such as people, culture, and media, will create our experience of life—and often, these inputs are not a reflection of the life we want. And so, in order to choose a better life for ourselves, we need to become mindful of the inputs that are currently influencing us and then make choices regarding what results we want in life and what inputs we either want to increase or decrease.

The good news is that we all have a choice (at least to some degree) regarding who we're around, the environment that we live in, and the media that we expose ourselves to. If we're not happy about our lives, we have the ability to choose a different life. It might not be easy or simple, just like it isn't easy or simple to transform our bodies by choosing what we eat. However, if we change our inputs and our influences, we're going to change our lives. In the following activity, you're going to find a series of questions that are going to help you evaluate the influences that you currently have in your life, and how being more deliberate about what you expose yourself to.

PEOPLE:

	1	2	3	4	5
Who are the 5 people you are around the most?					
If in 10 years you were going to become the average of these 5 people, what aspects of each person would you LIKE to become your traits? Which aspects would you DISLIKE?					
Do you WANT to be like these people? In what ways? If not, why?					
Who are the 5 people you are NOT around in person but who you either a) follow and learn from or b) look up to the most?					

In what way do you want to be more like each of these people?	What would you have to THINK differently in order to be more like each?	What would you have to DO differently to be more like each?	How can you spend more time with these people (or people like this?) (In person or through media.)	How would this impact your life?

CULTURE:

- What different cultures are you part of? (For example: nationality, region, religion, family history, community, school, interests, etc.)

- What core beliefs do you have about how life is supposed to be that you know were influenced by your culture?

- Do you WANT to believe and live this way?

- What would you change about your culture if you could?

- How would this impact your life?

MEDIA:

- What are the 3 top musicians or types of music you listen to?

- What do you feel because of the music you listen to?

- What are the top 3 TV shows or movies that you watch?

- What is the overall theme of them?

- What lessons do they tell you about life?

- Do you want to live the way your favorite musicians live? Why or why not?

- Do you want to live a life like the shows or movies you watch? Why or why not?

- Does the media you watch make you feel optimistic about the world or pessimistic?

- If you changed the media you watched, how would this impact your life?

INFORMATION:

- What are the 3 top sources of NEWS media (or other means of learning about the world) do you watch or read?

- What do you believe because of the information you learn here?

- Does the media you watch make you feel optimistic about the world or pessimistic?

- Does the news information you are consuming give you the whole story? How do you know?

- Do you believe that if you exposed yourself to different ideas that you would think differently?

- What would happen if you did? How would this impact your life?

SOCIAL MEDIA:

- Where do you spend your time on social media?

- How much time do you spend on average per day?

- Who do you follow the most that you know well?

- Who do you follow the most that you do not know?

- What do you think the people you follow value in life?

- What types of social media or specific people do you feel have a negative impact on how you feel and act?

- What positive influences are there?

- If you were going to change your social media consumption, what would you want to change and why?

- How would this impact your life?

DAY 18: BEING PRESENT WITH OTHERS

HOLDING SPACE

When you say, "how's it going?" to coworkers, store clerks, or even family, do you ever really stop to listen to the answer?

When your kid comes home from school and is telling you the longest story ever, are you looking them directly in the face and hanging on every word or are you distracted playing with your phone or cooking?

When your loved one arrives home, do you stop what you're doing to greet them like you care that they're there? If so, do you quickly turn around and go back to what you were doing?

When you eat dinner with your family, are you engaged and talking, or is everyone off in their own world?

And when you are talking with someone, how often are you TRULY listening without multi-talking, thinking about your rebuttal, or thinking about the things on your to-do list.

Be honest with yourself and consider, how often do you give another person your undivided attention?

It's important to practice being present with other people. When you're not present with them—when you are with them in the same room or even right next to them but your mind is elsewhere, you both miss out on the opportunity to truly connect, and you make the other person feel like they aren't valued.

All everyone wants is to be seen and heard.

In the movie Avatar the Navee greet each other by saying "I see you". This means they are honoring them by giving them their full attention AND also seeing the truth about the greatness of who they are. It's a beautiful way of acknowledging another person and expressing that they matter to you.

When I (Natalie) used to run a program I created for adolescents and their parents called the Parent Teen Challenge. The kids in this program were 11 to 17 years old and were court ordered to attend. They had just attended a bootcamp program the week before and they were attending my program to spend the day reconnecting with their parents and opening communication.

The last activity of the day was a process called "if you really knew me" in which the kid and the parents took turns talking, each for 2 minutes, sharing with the others "if you really knew me"... and then tell their truth. There were always a lot of tears and emotions, as this level of openness between families does not happen often. The reason the conversation was able to happen is because the whole day they had been developing trust with each other and, most importantly, during the activity they were all 100% focused on the other person. They were fully present with them.

What struck me was how many times the kids, and even the adults, would share with the group at the end that this was the first time in their lives that anyone had ever REALLY listened to them.

It was beautiful, but it was also sad to know how little true connection most people had.

Working with these families, week after week, and watching the power of presence, openness, and love was actually the trigger to my own personal transformation. When I saw the depths of life experience and connection that was possible, it helped me reflect on my own life and led me to make radical changes, including ending relationships, changing my career, and completely transformation myself from within.

I know firsthand the power of being fully present with another person. I have watched hundreds of lives be changed by the simple act of giving another undivided attention, truly listening, and seeing them for who they really are.

Giving another person your full presence is the biggest gift you could ever give.

When anyone you care about is seeking to connect with you, give them 100% of yourself, even if it is only for a minute or two. Stop what you're doing and be present with your 2-year old niece who is excited to see you and is tugging on your jacket. Rather than continuing to stare at the TV as if he doesn't exist, when your husband sits down next to you on the couch turn to him and acknowledge him with your full attention. When the new person at work introduces herself to you, stop and take the time to welcome her, ask about where she is from, and offer to help her connect to other people in the office, rather than quickly moving on and going to talk to your friend as if this new person isn't even there.

And when someone is having a hard time or is in pain, this is the most powerful time to be present with them. When someone is grieving or experiencing extreme challenges, it can be hard to know what to do or how to help. But the most powerful thing you can do is HOLD SPACE for that person—to simply be there with them.

Holding space means being present, open, and protective of the other person's needs. There is nothing you need to do and you don't need to try to fix anything. Simply give your attention. Witness their experience. Be compassionate. Be the awareness, the love, the space where the other person can go through whatever they're going through and not be alone. There are 6 key components to holding space for another person.

1. **Safety**. Gives them permission to be open, honest, genuine and vulnerable. Must have a sense of trust. Your complete attention and lack of trying to fix anything lets them know you are there for them.

2. **Attention.** Listen attentively without the need to respond, comment, or problem solve—unless they specifically ask you a question. Maintain eye contact and be free of distractions. Know that silence is the most powerful way to hold space with someone. Resist the urge to fill the empty space or speak unless you're asked to.

3. **Reflect.** If you are going to say something to the person, avoid the temptation to say the phrases many people tend to say when someone else is upset, such as: "I understand" (no, you don't), "it's going to be okay" (in some cases it won't, so don't say it). Instead, reflect what they tell you. For instance, if they share with you about something that happened, recap what they told you to confirm you understood them. If they express how they are feeling, affirm their emotion: "I can see this is really hard for you." or "I understand why you would feel that way." It's important to do this even if you do not understand.

4. **Suspend self-importance.** Always remember it's not about you in this moment. Put aside your personal concerns. Be humble and willing to endure the other person's intense emotions, even if they are directed at you. Even though you are trying to be compassionate, this is NOT the time to try to empathize by sharing something from your own life that makes you relate to what they're going through. It does NOT make someone feel better to know you have suffered too. Bringing it up only turns the focus toward you. Your goal is not to reassure them that they're not the only one who goes through this situation or that there will be a resolution one day,

your goal is to be there with them as they have their experience.

5. **Non-judgment.** Even if you have been through what this person is going through, you cannot fully understand their feelings. And if you assume that their experience is the same as yours you may judge them for reacting differently than you would. Your opinion of the situation and whether or not you agree with this person's perspective are not relevant and it is important to quiet your own mind and suspend judgment of the person's thoughts or emotions, even if they appear irrational to you. Allow them to have their experience.

6. **Compassion.** Even though you are allowing them to have their experience and accepting it as it is, that doesn't mean that you won't wish for them to feel better and hope for a desirable outcome for them. In many cases, simply being the loving presence that supports them during their hard time is enough to help ease the pain of that person. By holding space and being there for someone, it expresses to them "I don't want you to hurt, I am here to help" without you having to say a word. It is also okay to ask the person "Is there anything I could do to support you right now?" and then do what you can to grant them that wish. However, if the person says that there is nothing they need assistance with, you can continue to be with them and offer your presence. Of course, if the person asks to be alone, honor their wishes.

Take a few minutes to reflect on in what ways you can be more present with the people in your life.

- Who do you interact with every day? For each person, commit to 1 way you will be more present with them in the next 24 hours. What will you do differently?

- Who in your life do you know you have not been giving enough of your full attention to? What can you do to be fully present with this person or people?

- Is there anyone in your life going through challenging times? When and how might you be able to hold space for this person?

Your final challenge is to pick at least one stranger you interact with today to practice being fully present with, either by making full eye contact and thanking them, asking them how their day is going and really mean it, or another means of giving of yourself and truly seeing them.

I see you.

MINDFUL ARRIVALS

Whether you're arriving at work or arriving at home, do so mindfully

Many people arrive at work and are immediately triggered by the negative association of working and become stressed out. Take time to reflect on how you're feeling, set a positive intention for your day, put yourself into a good mood. Be grateful you have a job.

When arriving at home, especially if you have a family member to come home to, be mindful of the transition back home. Be there fully. Be present with your loved one.

Set an intention for how you're going to spend your time at home, what you'll do, with who, and how it will go.

Create a sanctuary for yourself. If there are aspects of your home life that are stressful, rather than reacting to the stressors, take time to reflect on why you feel the way you do and what you can do to minimize the stress.

DAY 19: RANDOM ACTS OF KINDNESS

MINDFULNESS WITH LOVE AND KINDNESS

Love and kindness are ways of expressing one's mindfulness to others. They are also wonderful states to experience during mindfulness meditation. One way to practice mindfulness with others is to offer acts of kindness. However, you can also give yourself and others the gift of loving-kindness through meditation itself, by feeling the emotions and sending the loving energy to others. First, let's look at acts of kindness. Then you will find two loving-kindness meditations.

Acts of kindness can help transform any mindfulness practice. It's a great way to put what you're learning into practice in the real world.

In fact, studies have shown that when we do an act of kindness it impacts both the person that is receiving it and the person doing it by releasing feel good chemicals and changing our state. Not only that, it also impacts others who witness the act of kindness. This is because contribution is one of our core human needs. We naturally want to contribute to those around us. When we practice mindfulness many times we focus on being aware of our self and our environment which is passive mindfulness. On the other hand when you practice acts of kindness you are practicing active mindfulness. This is because as you do your act of kindness you are in the present moment fully engaged in the moment. By being present with someone and offering a kind gesture, you are bringing you both into a state of full engagement with the present moment AND paying forward your positive thoughts by brightening someone's day.

One thing to keep in mind is that these acts of kindness do not have to be complicated or premeditated. In fact, they can be as simple as giving someone a smile, opening the door for someone, sharing gratitude with someone for an action they did, helping someone in need, and so on.

For example, when I (Joeel) was sick and bed ridden, I woke up one day to hear a lawn mower. I later found out that my neighbor had cut my lawn because he knew the condition I was in and that I was unable to do it. For him it was his random act of kindness and part of his mindfulness practice. When I told him that I wanted to give back to him he responded that he was just contributing to me like I have contributed to the life of others in my journey and that I should just accept the random act of kindness. Therefore, I am a true believer that there is a ripple affect that as you bless others you are also blessed in unexpected way.

Ask yourself, "what is an act of kindness that I can do today?"

LOVING-KINDNESS MEDITATION

Loving Kindness Meditation

- Become comfortable in your chair or cushion, sitting with a relaxed but straight, posture, with your shoulders relaxed. (*Pause*)…

- Allow your hands to rest comfortably in your lap. Gently close your eyes… (*Pause*)…

- Settling into awareness of the body…and the breath.

- Feeling into our body right now…noticing what's here.

- Open to whatever is to be experienced in the body in this moment
- Connecting to the breath… noticing the wave-like movements of the belly…
- In this practice, we'll be cultivating loving kindness. We all have within us, this natural capacity for lovingkindness. Or… friendship that is unconditional and open… gentle… supportive.
- Lovingkindness is a natural opening of a compassionate heart… to ourselves and to others. It's a wish that everyone be happy.
- We begin with developing lovingkindness toward ourselves…allowing our hearts to open with tenderness.
- Now, allow yourself to remember and open up to your basic goodness. You might remember times you have been kind or generous. You might recall your natural desire to be happy and not to suffer. If acknowledging your own goodness is difficult, look at yourself through the eyes of someone who loves you. What does that person love about you? Or, you may recall the unconditional love you felt from a beloved pet…
- It may help to use the imagination and to picture yourself as a young child standing before you…perhaps 4 or 5 years of age… if that allows tender feelings of kindness to flow more easily…
- And, as you experience this love…notice how you feel in your body. Maybe you feel some warmth…or heat in the face. A smile…a sense of expansiveness. This is lovingkindness, a natural feeling that is accessible to all of us…always. Resting with this feeling of open, unconditional love for a few minutes … (*Pause*)
- Letting yourself bask in the energy of lovingkindness…breathing it in…and breathing it out…inviting feelings of peace and acceptance…
- Begin now to wish yourself well by extending words of loving kindness to yourself.

Below you will find phrases that we have used in our own practice, however, you're invited to alter these phrases and choose whatever words express your wishes of loving kindness toward yourself and others.

And now, offering these words in your mind for yourself…

- May I be filled with lovingkindness
- May I be held in loving kindness…

- May I feel connected and calm…
- May I accept myself just as I am…
- May I be happy…
- May I know the natural joy of being alive…

And, now repeating in the mind these words of friendship and kindness to yourself once again…

- May I be filled with lovingkindness
- May I be held in loving kindness…
- May I feel connected and calm…
- May I accept myself just as I am…
- May I be happy…
- May I know the natural joy of being alive

Now you can open the circle of lovingkindness by bringing to mind someone who is dear to you. Someone whom you care about and who has always been supportive. Reflect on this person's basic goodness, sensing what it is in particular that you love about him or her. In your heart feel your appreciation for this dear one, and begin your simple offering…

- May you be filled with lovingkindness
- May you be held in lovingkindness…
- May you feel my love now…
- May you accept yourself just as you are…
- May you be happy…
- May you know the natural joy of being alive…

Now bring to mind a "neutral" person. This is someone you might see regularly but don't know well…It might be a neighbor, a grocery store clerk.

- Bring this person to mind now, and repeat the words of loving kindness…
- May you be filled with lovingkindness
- May you be held in lovingkindness…
- May you feel my love now…
- May you accept yourself just as you are…
- May you be happy…
- May you know the natural joy of being alive…

And now, if it's possible for you, bring to mind someone with whom you've had a difficult relationship. Perhaps it's someone you don't like to feel sympathy or compassion for. Seeing if it's possible to let go of feelings of resentment and dislike for this person. Reminding yourself to see this person as a whole being…deserving of love and kindness. As someone who feels pain and anxiety…as someone who also suffers.

Seeing if it's possible to extend to this person the words of loving kindness in your mind…

- May you be filled with lovingkindness
- May you be held in lovingkindness…
- May you feel my love now…
- May you accept yourself just as you are…
- May you be happy…
- May you know the natural joy of being alive…

Now, allow your awareness to open out in all directions…yourself, a dear one, a neutral person and a difficult person…and of all beings… humans and animals living everywhere…living in richness, poverty, war, peace, hunger, abundance…Aware of all the joys and sorrows that all beings experience…

- May all beings be filled with lovingkindness…
- May all beings be happy…
- May all beings awaken and be free…
- May all beings be happy…

And now, bringing this practice to a close by coming back to extend kindness to yourself. Sitting for a while and basking in the energy of loving kindness that may have been generated here.

DAY 20: ESTABLISHING A MINDFULNESS ROUTINE

In a separate worksheet you will be addressing establishing a formal meditation practice. This worksheet is designed to help you determine how you will continue to integrate mindfulness into your ongoing daily life.

- My favorite mindfulness exercises that I experienced during this experience:
- Which of these exercises do I want to integrate into my everyday life?
- How will you integrate mindfulness into your morning routine?
- How will you integrate mindfulness into your bedtime routine?

MINDFUL MORNING ROUTINE

When we first wake up we have a new beginning, an opportunity to re-set, and a chance to set the tone for the rest of the day. This means that this is the best time to follow through on a new routine as well as to start the day of being mindful. In fact, Tim Ferris a best-selling author and a highly acclaimed entrepreneur has interviewed some of the most successful people in the world and what he found was that they all had a morning mindfulness routine.

Keep in mind that we are all different and we have different needs of what will work for us. Therefore, the most important thing is finding a routine that fits you.

Here are a few tips:

- **Prepare the night nefore.** To have a successful morning routine you must plan for it. Writing it down and scheduling it in is a pow-erful way to let our mind know what our intentions are. Therefore, consider what you will need and make time for it. To be able to do this make sure that you are waking up earlier than you need to give your self-time. The last thing you want is to be rushed when you are trying to be mindful. Therefore, you want to have enough time that you can start your morning slowly without unnecessary stress. Some of the things that you can also do the night before to make your morning more flexible is making or prepping your lunch the night before and picking your clothes. Of course, getting a good night sleep will also impact your day so make sure that you get a good night sleep.

- **Starting your morning.** Wake up at least 30 minutes earlier and make sure your alarm is one that is soothing. It can be a song or nature sounds instead of an alarm that will put your body in a state of stress. Not a morning person? Remember that you can't expect to make drastic changes to your morning routine. For example, if you are used to waking up late then cutting that by 2 hours may be unreasonable. Change takes time so make changes to your night routine, so you can go to sleep earlier and change morning routines gradually. Or, simply use morning rituals that can be done during your existing routing so that it doesn't take you extra time.

- **Stretch and breathe.** When you first wake up, stretch and take five deep breaths as you connect with your body.

- **Practice gratitude.** Name five things out loud that you're grateful for. These could be things that you are looking forward to, things form your day before, how comfortable your bed was, or anything you can think of. Starting your day with gratitude will set a positive emotional state for the day.

- **State a mantra or affirmation to yourself. For example:**

  Today is a new day. It is a gift, an opportunity for new opportunities. I wake into this new day with optimism and openness to the blessings it will hold. I intent to live today fully and mindfully and appreciate every moment of it.

- **Ignore your devices.** Research has found that 80% of smartphone users check their phones within 15 minutes of waking up. This takes away from your time of being with yourself and being mindful of what you are creating with your day. Plus, since most smartphone users are checking their email or social media, doing this also allows exposure to others to determine the thoughts and emotions that start their day. Therefore, make sure that you are being intentional and deciding what you want to experience and consider that your phone probably does not contain your intentions, desired emotions, or mindfulness.

- **Change it up.** Remember that you do not have to do the same thing repeatedly, you can experiment with different routines and rituals as long as you commit to a regular schedule. This will help you find the morning processes that truly resonate with you and be able to keep things fresh so that it makes it easier to stay mindful.

- **Create a morning routine that engages your mind and your body.** Your routine should be one that engages your mind and body so that you can start your day feeling energized and ready to move forward.

- **Let the light in:** There is a reason movies tend to show people opening the drapes in the morning. Letting the light in signals to your brain that it's time to come back to full awareness. If you're waking up before the sun rises, turn on the lights.

- **Get wet:** You can splash cold or hot water on your face depending on what feels right for you. You can also jump in the shower to start your morning. Many high performers report jumping into cold water to jumpstart their day.

- **Use essential oil:** Using essential oils can stimulate your senses and help you feel energized, such as taking deep inhalations of peppermint. You can also combine aromatherapy with your mindfulness exercises or meditations.

- **Exercise:** When you exercise your body produces endorphins and adrenaline which can give you a boost to start your day. Exercise is a great mindfulness practice if you really pay attention to the moves of your body, whether you're going for a walk, doing stretching or yoga, or hitting the gym. You can also listen to a mindfulness exercise or mediation while you exercise.

- **Meditate.** Many people who meditate regularly do it first thing in the morning. If you would like your formal meditation practice to be in the morning, consider at what point in your existing routine you would be most able to integrate meditation. Immediately upon waking up? After you use the bathroom? Before or after your coffee? Where will you do it? If you are meditating in your bed, make sure to set a gentle alarm, as some people tend to fall asleep if they meditate in the morning. If you tend to fall back asleep, consider moving your meditation to another time of the day when you are better able to focus.

- **Make it a group experience.** One of the best ways to stay committed to a morning routine is to get others involved. This will help develop support and hold you accountable. This person may be someone in your home such as a family member, a person that can meet you virtually or that you reach out to each other. It can even be a virtual group that meets to meditate, or a physical or virtual class that you take in the morning.

Here are otheractivities you can consider including in your version of a mindful morning routine:

- Read

- Spend time in nature
- Prepare / eat healthy food
- Breathwork
- Drink tea (or coffee) mindfully
- Write down a daily intention for yourself
- Play or listen to music
- Watch something that will make you laugh
- Keep a journal
- Do something creative (write, draw, paint, create)
- Create something or work on your passion project

MINDFUL BEDTIME ROUTINE

As we look at creating a nighttime or bedtime routine that helps us be more mindful and helps us relax and get a good night sleep, it's important to remember that everyone is different and that we all have different needs so it's about finding what works for you. Whatever it is that you decide to do in order to be mindful during your nighttime routine, the key is to make it a habit. Once you've established a routine, it acts as a trigger to your brain so that as you start your routine your brain knows it's time to wind down. Research shows that our brain is calmed by repetition and comforted by consistency. Not only is practicing mindfulness at bedtime beneficial to your mindfulness practice, it will also help you have better sleep and wake up in a better state.

Chances are you already have a routine you do before bed, even if it's simply brushing your teeth, taking a shower or using the bathroom. You can simply make it a point to be mindful during your existing bedtime routine by paying close attention to the steps of brushing your teeth, the way the toothbrush feels in your mouth, the sounds and smells of a nice hot shower, how it feels as the water hits different parts of your body, the way that the water looks as it falls from the shower head. You can also take a few minutes as you crawl into bed to be mindful of how it feels to lay down and rest. The softness of your blanket, the way the pillow cushions your head, the stillness in your body, the silence in the room.

In addition to the ample opportunities to practice mindfulness during your bedtime routine, last thing at night is also a great time to practice some of the mindfulness or meditation techniques you have learned. Meditating at night is a great way to calm the mind and prepare it for restful sleep. If you plan to add one of the practices you learned into your nighttime routine, consider when and where you will do it and whether you will need any supplies, such as guided meditation audio, music, headphones, etc.

Here are some additional tips for optimizing your bedtime routine, both to increase your mindfulness and to have more restful sleep.

- **Electronic devices.** Our current society loves electronic devices whether it's your phone, tablet, or tv. However, many studies find that we should not use them an hour before we sleep since they stimulate our brain, the light that they produce interferes with our internal clock, and the activities or content we access through these devices can create stress.

- **Declutter.** Your bedroom is your sanctuary, so keep it decluttered as it will help the brain relax.

- **Dim the lights.** Lights are a trigger to our biological clock of when and if we should be sleeping. Therefore, dimming the lights or turning them off helps the mind know it should be shutting down.

- **Listen to music or nature sounds.** Sounds can help our body feel relaxed and can also serve as a trigger for the body that it's time for bed if you use the same sounds on a constant basis. Of course, you do not want music that is too stimulating.

- **Write down any ideas that pop into your mind as you're going to bed, especially things that need to be remembered.** By writing it down you release your mind from the need to keep the thought active. You might even find that your mind is relaxed and therefore creative at night and you may find great new ideas popping up. Writing them down is better than trying to repress them.

- **Complete a 5 minutes journal entry.** This does not have to be complicated, it can be as simple as writing down 5 things that you are grateful for.

- **Read.** You can also take 20 minutes to read to relax the brain. Just make sure that you are not reading work related material or things that are too stimulating. Ideally read in another room so that your mind does not associate stimulation with your bed.

- **Drink tea.** Some teas are great to help relax the body. Chamomile, Valerian Root, and Lavender are among the ones that are associated with sleep.

- **Use essential oils.** Aromatherapy has been shown to be a great trigger for the mind, and using a soothing scent before bed every night tells the mind that it is time to calm and rest.

- **Don't lie awake for hours.** If you find you are unable to fall asleep quickly, do not beat yourself up or continue to lay in bed feeling frustrated, which increases anxiety and stress. Accept however you are feeling and the fact that you are still awake, and remember that all thoughts and emotions will eventually pass. Your body will sleep when it's ready. Focus on your breathing or use one of your favorite mindfulness techniques and be patient with yourself. Tell yourself it's okay if your mind is active. It will tire itself out like a toddler and will eventually crash. Your body knows how to take care of itself and will find its way to rest. It takes the average person between 20 and 30 minutes to fall asleep. If you are still up after 30-45 minutes, it is beneficial to get up briefly and take 15 minutes to conduct some of your bedtime routines or favorite mindfulness practices.

DAYS OF THE WEEK MINDFULNESS ROUTINE

Whether you are looking to continue to support your mindfulness practice after the 21-day challenge or you are a service provider that wants to support your client long term creating a daily mindfulness schedule can be powerful. Therefore, for each day pick a specific mindfulness strategy and activity. You can always change it with time, however, the consistency can be powerful because it will help you start incorporating the activities on an unconscious level. This means that you won't even to have to think about it your mind and body will naturally follow the process.

Dr. Amit Sood, the chair of the Mayo Mind Body Initiative provides a great template to work from. Remember that you can change it to make it fit for you or your clients.

1. **Monday: Gratitude** – Gratitude can be a powerful force. Therefore, for the day find things that you are grateful for. As you go through your day you can write down the things that come up that you are grateful, and you can also do a gratitude and a loving kindness meditation.

2. **Tuesday: Compassion** – Compassion for ourselves and others is essential for creating a more loving and kinder space around us. Therefore, for the day set the intention to decrease any suffering in yourself and others that may come up throughout your day.

3. **Wednesday: Acceptance** – Acceptance can be challenging for many people. This is something that takes practice but with time can be powerful in decreasing stress and increasing happiness and wellbeing. When it comes to acceptance, we are talking about acceptance of yourself as you are and accepting others for who they are. In other words, yourself as you are and others as they are. This allows us to look at our self and others without judgement and without trying to change them. This does not mean that we don't strive to improve where we are at or that we must accept people behaviors that are detrimental to us. By allowing ourselves to accept things for what they are we are better able to clearly see what reality is. Keep in mind that there is an acceptance meditation in this book that you can do.

4. **Thursday: Meaning and Purpose** – Living a life of purpose is essential. Therefore, spending time reflecting on your purpose is essential. Therefore, think about your purpose in life and what brings you meaning. Also keep in mind that as you continue this routine that you will get more and more clarity every week. You can also reflect on what steps you are taking to do more of those things that produce meaning and lead you towards your purpose.

5. **Friday: Forgiveness** – Forgiveness is a critical part of releasing and being able to let go of baggage that may be holding you back. It is important to reflect and forgive yourself first. For example, in my life after my (Joeel) brother passed away I had to do a lot of work to forgive myself and the feeling that I could have helped in some way. The unforgiveness was impacting every aspect of my life. Therefore, by forgiving myself I was able to let go of the chains that where holding me back and impacting my health. You should also look at people that you may need to forgive. Remember as the quote from. Marianne Williamson: Unforgiveness is like drinking poison yourself and waiting for the other person to die. As you forgive keep in mind that there are many ways to do this. You can express forgiveness to yourself or others. You can write a letter make a phone call. You can do a forgiveness meditation. The most important part is to do something symbolic. The mind sometimes needs a symbolic gesture to feel like it is releasing something. Therefore, this can be writing it down and then stating to yourself that you release it as you rip the piece of paper.

6. **Saturday: Celebration** – This is one of our favorite things to do and that many people do not take enough time to do. That is celebrate your success as well as the little things in your life and the life of those around you. This celebration can be something simple or something that is complex. The important part is that the celebration is something that you enjoy. Remember that by celebrating you are helping reinforce the positive things in your life and empowering yourself and boosting your confidence moving forward.

7. **Sunday: Reflection** – On this day reflect on your week or month. This can also be any specific time that you would like to reflect on. Reflection is critical to creating long term change and understanding what is working and what is not working and what ways we can change improve. You can choose to reflect through meditation, journaling, prayer, or simply creating awareness of the time that you are reflecting on.

DAY 21: ESTABLISHING A FORMAL MEDITATION PRACTICE

Understand Your Why

It's time to put everything you've learned together and create a formal meditation practice. But first, we want to congratulate you on making it this far! The mindfulness that you've developed at this point will permanently alter the level of awareness that you have in daily life. But, if you want to experience the full benefits of mindfulness and meditation and continue the habit that you've developed in these last few weeks, it's time to establish a formal meditation practice.

The following exercise will help you establish the momentum and the plan for creating a long-term, formal habit of meditation and mindfulness. At the end you will find a list of questions. The first thing you have to look at is understanding your "why". To be able to maintain any new habit and create long-term change, you need to have a clear reason why you want to create that change. The stronger the reason is for why you want to do it, the higher the chances are that you're going to follow through.

If you're trying to create a meditation practice because someone else tells you that you should, or because it's trendy, then you're probably not going to have the commitment to follow through in those moments when you're just not feeling in the mood.

On the other hand, if you're doing it because you genuinely want more energy, or maybe you want to keep your anxiety or stressful thoughts under control, then you're going to be more willing to follow through. Ask yourself, what is the real reason why you want to establish a meditation practice? What benefits will you receive from doing it? How is it going to change your life? Also, look at what will happen if you do not continue to use the meditation or mindfulness techniques that you've learned regularly.

- What is the real reason you want to establish a meditation practice?

- What benefits will you receive from doing it?

- How will your life change?

- What will happen if you do NOT continue to use meditation or mindfulness techniques regularly?

Start Small

Remember to be reasonable with yourself. If you try to commit to too much too soon, or you set unrealistic expectations for yourself, you will become discouraged or overwhelmed. The goal is to find a way to fit meditation into your life's existing patterns so that it isn't too disruptive and it's easy to habituate. The key to a successful meditation practice is to start small and simple. Choose 1 or 2 of your favorite mindfulness or meditation exercises and commit to doing them every day. Choose mindfulness exercises that you will have the opportunity to use daily, such as mindful eating, walking or driving. Also, select your favorite meditation(s) and choose a specific time of day that you will practice your meditation every day.

- How much time per day feels completely reasonable for you to meditate?

- What time of day would be the easiest for you to commit to it?

- If you're starting small, what would be your initial meditation goal?

- In the long term, if you would like to increase your practice, what would your goal be?

Schedule Your Meditation

Having a schedule is a key to success.

- Where will you put your schedule? (Day planner, phone reminder, wall calendar, etc.)

- How long will your sessions be?

- When will you do them?

Here are several examples: 8 minutes twice a day after lunch and before bed, 2 15-minute walks before breakfast and as an afternoon break, 3 3-minute breathing exercises while listening to one of your favorite songs.

Tie It to an Existing Pattern

The best way to create any new habit is to piggyback off a routine you already have. This is why so many people tend to meditate in the morning or at night. This way, they can integrate their meditation into their existing morning and bedtime routines. Since you already remember to do these routines every day, you will always remember to do your meditation practice. Another idea is to listen to a meditation when you get in the car before you leave for work.

- What habit or routine could you add your meditation practice to?

- How will you work this into the schedule you identified?

Create the Environment

It's also important to choose a good environment for your meditation. You can practice mindfulness or meditation basically anywhere, but having a dedicated location, especially for the longer sessions that you do, it's going to help you establish the habit and enjoy the process more. With time, just entering the space will help you relax because you're going to condition your mind to associate that space with your meditation practice. For example, is there a place in your house that you could set up a yoga mat or a comfy chair that you could use to meditate? You can fill the space with things that will inspire you, such as photos, candles, oils, or anything else that inspires you.

- Where will you be practicing your meditations?

- What can you do to make it more comfortable (such as a yoga mat or a chair)?

- How will you fill that space with things that will inspire you such as photos, candles, incense or anything else that will inspire you?

Choose a Method

It's important to know what type of meditation practice you're going to be doing during your allotted time, ahead of time. For example, you could choose to do breath work, listen to a guided meditation, do a body scan, or any other meditation you like. You don't necessarily have to do the same one every time, however you don't want to be waiting to the last minute to decide what you're going to be doing because you don't want to waste your allotted time making the decision or finding the audio file, if necessary.

- Which meditation processes are your favorite?

- Which would you like to do regularly?

- Are there any particular ones you want to work into the schedule you created?

- What supplies or audio files do you need and where will you keep them to make sure they're available?

Create Accountability

You also want to consider if you will need help holding yourself accountable to your new habit. For example, you can start your new meditation practice with a friend or a family member, either doing the exercise together or checking in with each other daily to act as each other's accountability partner. For a long time, we used a group chat with family members to hold each other accountable when we were all committing to walking 10,000 steps a day.

If you're going to be your own accountability, one method is to give yourself a reward for your accomplishment of reaching your meditation goals. Meditation itself is a reward, but when starting any new habit, giving yourself a reward every time that you achieve it reinforces the new behavior, making it become habituated faster.

- What method will you use to create accountability?

And lastly, it's important to continually assess what's working and what's not working. You might find that mornings work better than evenings for you or that some types of meditations work better than others. If you want mindfulness and meditation to be part of your everyday life, it's not a matter of IF it's going to work for you, it's a matter of experimenting to determine what optimizes your experience and your ability to do it consistently.

Take the time to sit down and really think about and write down your plan for how you're going to implement this into your daily life. You owe it to yourself to commit to providing yourself the space to become your best self.

TAKE THE
ONLINE
COURSE!

Learn directly from instructors Joeel & Natalie!

The 21 Day Mindfulness & Meditation Challenge online course covers the content in this book through video lectures and printable worksheets that bring the content in this book to life! This a great, fun way to review and learn the material!

ENROLL FOR FREE!
Visit: www.transformationacademy.com/mindfulnessbook/
Use coupon code: *mindfulnessbook*

If you are a life coach (or want to be), enroll in the **Mindfulness Life Coach CERTIFICATION** program, which includes all content covered in this book, plus additional training for how to use these tools and processes with clients!

UPGRADE FOR ONLY $97!
(That's 50% off!)
Visit: www.transformationacademy.com/mindfulnessbook/
Use coupon code: *mindfulnesscoach*

PLUS, **save 50%** on all of our 60+ other courses!

Use coupon code:
mindfulnessbook50

MEET THE AUTHORS:

Joeel & Natalie Rivera

Joeel and Natalie Rivera are freedom junkies and prolific content creators who have launched over a dozen businesses. They have also been coaching, speaking, writing, and teaching for more than a decade.

Through their online education company Transformation Academy, they empower life coaches, INDIEpreneurs and transformation junkies to create a purpose-driven life and business and master the power of their mind so they can create their destiny.

Joeel is a former psychology professor with a Master's Degree in Counseling and Education and has been studying happiness for his dissertation for a Ph.D. in Psychology.

After almost losing it all in 2014 due to a sudden illness after traveling overseas, they converted their workshops, coaching and training programs into online courses. Today, they've created more than 85 online courses, taken by more than 750,000 students from 200 countries (at the time of this writing).

They believe that entrepreneurship is the ultimate form of empowerment. They believe in turning pain into purpose. And, they believe in the democratization of education and, therefore, make their programs available at a price that is within reach of students worldwide.

WWW.TRANSFORMATIONACADEMY.COM

Printed in Great Britain
by Amazon

23491013R00076